PERSONAL FITNESS

LOOKING GOOD—FEELING GOOD

CHARLES S. WILLIAMS
University of Florida

EMMANOUEL G. HARAGEONES
Escambia County Schools, Florida

DEWAYNE J. JOHNSON
Florida State University

CHARLES D. SMITH
University of South Florida

FOURTH EDITION

KENDALL/HUNT PUBLISHING COMPANY
4050 Westmark Drive   Dubuque, Iowa 52002

Cover images: Rollerbladers, Image © PhotoDisc 1998; Runners and Weight
Lifter, Photos © Kendall/Hunt Publishing Company by Ron Franklin; Food
images, Images courtesy of Corel

Copyright © 1986, 1993, 1995, 2000 by Kendall/Hunt Publishing Company

ISBN 0-7872-4726-X

Library of Congress Catalog Card Number: 98-066603

Printed in the United States of America
10 9 8 7 6 5 4

CONTENTS

1 **LOOKING GOOD—FEELING GOOD** X

Personal Fitness Is a Personal Matter
Physical Fitness Is a Trend
What Affects Your Attitude Toward Physical
   Fitness?
What Is Physical Fitness?
Primary Health Risk Factors
Contributing Health Risk Factor
Benefits of Exercise
Summary
Study Questions

2 **COMPONENTS OF FITNESS** 16

Analyzing Physical Fitness
Health-Related Fitness
Skill-Related Fitness
Fitness Assessment
Interpreting Assessment Results
Goal Setting
Summary
Study Questions

3 **GOAL SETTING FOR TEENAGERS** 32

Teen Years: A Topsy-Turvy Time
Taking Control of Your Health and Fitness
What Are Goals?
What Is Goal Setting?
Goal Setting Is Like a Ladder
Goal Setting Steps
Goal Setting in Action
Summary
Study Questions

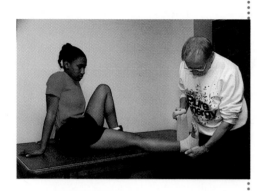

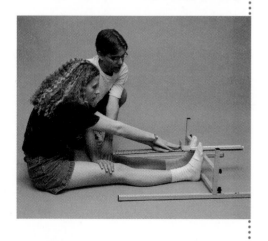

④ GUIDELINES FOR EXERCISE　　**46**

Getting Started
What You Wear Can Make A
　　Difference
Exercising in Hot Weather
Exercising in Cold Weather
Additional Safety Precautions
Warming Up
Cooling Down
Common Injuries
Summary
Study Questions

⑤ PRINCIPLES OF TRAINING　　**62**

Efficient and Safe Training
Principle of Overload
Principle of Progression
Principle of Specificity
Summary
Study Questions

⑥ FLEXIBILITY　　**72**

What Is Flexibility?
Why Is Flexibility Important?
Types of Stretching
Application of Training Principles
Flexibility Safety Precautions
Flexibility Assessment
Goal Setting for Flexibility
Flexibility Exercises
Harmful Stretching Positions
Summary
Study Questions

⑦ **CARDIOVASCULAR FITNESS**　　86

Why Is Cardiovascular Fitness Important?
Circulatory and Respiratory Systems
Monitoring the Heart
Cardiovascular Disease
Cardiovascular Benefits of Exercise
Application of Training Principles
Goal Setting for Cardiovascular Fitness
Summary
Study Questions

⑧ **MUSCULAR FITNESS**　　104

Muscular Strength and Endurance
Myths About Weight Training
Muscle Fiber Composition
Methods of Developing Muscular Fitness
Application of Training Principles
Goal Setting for Abdominal Strength and
　Endurance
Goal Setting for Upper Body Strength
Weight Training Considerations
Muscular Fitness Exercises
Summary
Study Questions

⑨ **NUTRITION**　　130

Historical Use of Food
Acquired Experiences with Food
Food and Its Relation to Health
Essential Nutrients
Water: An Essential Element
The New Food Label
The Food Guide Pyramid

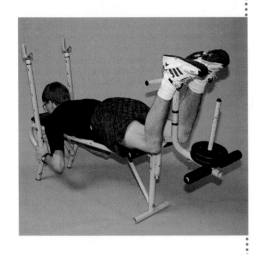

Determining Daily Calorie Requirements
Daily Diet
Summary
Study Questions

10 BODY COMPOSITION AND WEIGHT CONTROL   152

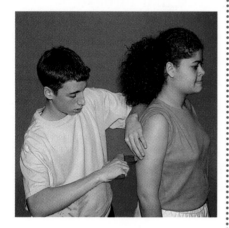

Rx for Looking Good and Feeling Good
Body Types
Body Composition
Methods of Measuring Body Fat
Importance of Weight Control
Weight Loss, Weight Gain, and Weight
    Maintenance
Caloric Cost of Physical Activities
Permanent Weight Control Methods
Goal Setting for Body Composition
Eating Disorders
Weight Control Misconceptions
Summary
Study Questions

11 STRESS   172

Case Study: Sammy's Story
What Is Stress?
What Causes Stress?
How Does Your Body React to Stress?
How Does Stress Affect You?
What Are the Effects of Negative Stress?
Developing a Stress Management Program
Stress Diversion Activities
Negative Coping Techniques You Should
    Avoid

Summary
Study Questions

12 **CONSUMER ISSUES** **190**

You the Consumer
What Influences Your Buying Decisions?
Have You Been Ripped Off?
Spot Reduction: The Big Myth
False Advertising
Exercise Gadgets and Gimmicks
Drugs and Weight Control
Anabolic Steroids
Are Health Clubs Worth the Money?
Tips on Identifying False Advertising
What Can You Do To Combat False
   Advertising?
Summary
Study Questions

13 **EVALUATION OF ACTIVITIES** **204**

Which Activities Are Best?
Categories of Activities
Considerations Before Selecting Activities
Summary
Study Questions

14 **DESIGNING YOUR OWN
PROGRAM** **220**

Develop a Total Personal Fitness Program
Starting Your Program
Designing Your Personal Fitness Program
Steps in Designing Vanessa's Personal Fitness
   Program

Keep It Going
Summary
Study Questions

APPENDIX   **235**

BIBLIOGRAPHY   **245**

GLOSSARY   **247**

INDEX   **257**

PREFACE

This book could be one of the most meaningful books you will read in school. The primary goal of this book is to help people help themselves. It is important that you assume control and responsibility for your lifestyle. This book will help you better understand your personal capabilities and enable you to establish a personal fitness program based on nutrition, stress management, and exercise.

If physical activity can be incorporated into your lifestyle in an appropriate manner, it will unquestionably enhance your physical appearance. When you enhance your physical appearance, you also enhance the way you feel about yourself. Guiding you to help yourself look and feel better is what this book is all about. It is important to remember that there are hereditary traits over which you have no control. These traits include height, bone structure, type of body build, and facial features. Beyond these factors, however, you do have control over what you can be like in a physical sense.

We believe that **looking good and feeling good** is of great importance to everyone. We also believe that the vast majority of people can improve their bodies in terms of fitness. When that occurs, bodies become more attractive, resulting in people feeling good about themselves. By improving our bodies in some way, we take control of a part of our life and gain a sense of achievement and self-confidence. We will have accomplished something important to us that was not easy. When we achieve physical improvement, we are affected in more than just a physical way.

Since we are very complex beings, something that affects one aspect of our lives tends to affect other aspects of our lives. If people succeed in losing a few pounds, they gain a sense of pride because they made something happen; they feel in control of themselves and in control of a part of their life. What happens when people are successful? They are much more likely to be successful again because, as the old saying goes, nothing succeeds like success. This book is designed to help **you** be successful.

Our intention is to motivate you to become physically active. More importantly, we want you to develop a value for participation in meaningful physical activity. We believe strongly in your ability to take charge of the health and physical fitness aspects of your life. Good luck in your pursuit of self-improvement.

Charles S. Williams
Emmanouel G. Harageones
Dewayne J. Johnson
Charles D. Smith

LOOKING GOOD—FEELING GOOD

1

CHAPTER OBJECTIVES

As you read this chapter, look for answers to these key questions:

- Why is physical fitness a personal matter?
- Why do some people neglect their health by choosing not to participate in physical activity?
- What is physical fitness?
- What are the primary health risk factors and which ones may be controlled?
- What benefits are gained by exercising?

Success does not mean being the best, but doing your best.

PERSONAL FITNESS IS A PERSONAL MATTER

Do you know anyone who doesn't want to look as good as possible or to feel as good as possible? Probably not. It is only natural to want to look and feel good. The fact is that everyone has a great deal of control over this desire. Although you inherit your body type from your parents and grandparents, you can still control the feelings and attitudes you have about yourself. One of the factors that determines how you feel about yourself is the condition of your body. If you are pleased with the condition of your body, then chances are you will feel good about yourself totally.

Personal fitness is a **personal** matter. The word **personal** is a key word to remember. Try not to compare yourself to anyone else when working on self-improvement in physical fitness. Take pride in seeing yourself improve throughout this course. One of the most important things that will help you to experience success in improving how you look and feel is your **attitude.** Try to keep an open mind about personal fitness. Do not let others influence you in a negative way. Always try your best and give 100 percent. If you let others influence you in the wrong way, you will be the loser. Keeping a positive attitude can make a tremendous difference in any dimension of your life. This is certainly true when it comes to physical fitness and lifestyle.

"Hi. We hope you are tuned to improving your bodies. Being in good physical shape can mean a lot to all of us. See you at the end of the book."

PHYSICAL FITNESS IS A TREND

During the past 15 years, there has been a remarkable awakening of interest in physical fitness. Walkers, joggers, roller bladers, and bikers move through parks and along highways. Tennis and racquetball courts are filled to capacity, as are swimming pools. Health clubs and fitness centers are extremely popular. You probably have friends who engage in personal fitness programs. Physical fitness should be an important part of everyone's lifestyle.

Not long ago, it was common for people to get excited about some form of exercise, do it regularly for a period of time, then lose enthusiasm, and stop. This practice is called a **fad**. For many people, however, interest in physical fitness has persisted for many years and continues to be part of their lifestyle. When the interest in something, such as physical fitness, lasts for a long time, it is called a **trend**. Physical fitness continues to be a trend in this country. This is good news since personal fitness is such an important aspect of achieving greater self-respect and expanding your potential for a happy life.

SURGEON GENERAL'S REPORT ON PHYSICAL ACTIVITY

Many people are excited about their physical fitness programs and have active lifestyles. However, research studies continue to show that a large percentage of adults are not very fit and are overweight and out of shape. For example, the recently published **Surgeon General's Report on Physical Activity and Health** (1996) summarizes many research studies and the key finding is that people of all ages can improve the quality of their lives through a lifetime of moderate physical activity. While it is a fact that physical activity can help each of us live healthier, happier and more fulfilled lives, one of the most alarming findings of this report is that physical activity declines dramatically during the high school years. This is a dangerous trend when you consider the fact that regular physical activity reduces the risk of developing or dying from some of the leading causes of illness and death in the United States.

Are any members of your family inactive and over weight? If you, or any of your friends are in this category, this personal fitness course will give you an opportunity to start building a healthier lifestyle. That can be a rewarding process and you may find this course to be one of the most beneficial courses you will take in high school.

WHAT AFFECTS YOUR ATTITUDE TOWARD PHYSICAL FITNESS?

Since feeling good about your body is such an important part of self-image and self-concept, why do some people have a negative attitude toward improving their bodies? Several answers to this question will be discussed in this course, but you may have a few of your own to add.

LACK OF ATHLETIC ABILITY

Due to a lack of understanding of physical fitness, many people think that being a fast runner or a good ballplayer is part of being physically fit. Consequently, those students who do not have a good athletic background feel they cannot become physically fit. This way of thinking is unfortunate because you do not have to be a skilled person to be physically fit. Your experience in this course can be personally satisfying regardless of your athletic background.

PAST EXPERIENCE ON PHYSICAL FITNESS TESTS

Some people have had negative experiences being tested for physical fitness. Possible reasons for this feeling are a misunderstanding of what physical fitness is, a lack of preparation prior to taking the fitness test and consequently failing one or more parts of the test. Either of these reasons could affect your attitude about physical fitness.

PAST EXPERIENCE WITH YOUTH SPORTS

Another possible reason for the development of negative attitudes toward physical fitness is youth sports. It is estimated that over 20 million young people, ages 5 to 16, play youth sports in this country. Youth sports can be great experiences for the participants. However, a high percentage of young athletes, both male and female, drop out of youth sports at a relatively early age. The main reason is that the pressure to win increases at some point, and they stop having fun and begin to feel inferior to others. Adolescent psychologists believe many young people develop a negative attitude toward themselves, and this may carry over to attitudes toward their physical capabilities.

Heredity plays a role in your body type.

HEREDITY PLAYS A ROLE

The society we live in rewards slimness and athletic ability to a high degree. Many young women believe they should look like Miss America. Young men are expected to have lean, muscular bodies. As you are aware, very few people have the figure or body shape they perceive as being ideal. It is difficult to define what is meant by the ideal body shape, but the **thin-is-in** attitude prevails.

It is important to understand the role heredity plays in a person's body type or build. Bone structure influences a person's measurements. Naturally a person with large bones will have larger measurements than a person with small bones. However, people with either bone structure can have attractive body shapes. Regardless of your body type, keep in mind that you can maximize the attractiveness of your body through a proper physical fitness and wellness program.

1-3

MEDIA INFLUENCE

Another factor that may foster negative attitudes about physical fitness in the minds of teens is the **media** coverage in magazines, television, and newspapers ads. While the media has presented positive aspects of health and fitness, there have also been some negative aspects. Ads selling products to improve appearance frequently do so in a deceptive manner. They suggest that every young woman should have a slender and attractive body and every young man should have a muscular and well-shaped body. Some young people will not be able to attain these levels of appearance and, consequently, will develop feelings of inadequacy. Along the same line, some parents are also influenced by the media in terms of what young people should look like. As a result, they sometimes put pressure on their children to lose weight or to do something else to improve their appearance. The following section explains why some people are unable to attain the body image promoted in the media.

WHAT IS PHYSICAL FITNESS?

SPEED?
POWER?
AGILITY?
BODY FAT?
CARDIOVASCULAR?
COORDINATION?
BALANCE?
STRENGTH?
FLEXIBILITY?
MUSCULAR ENDURANCE?
REACTION TIME?

Confused about physical fitness?

Definitions of physical fitness vary widely. It is easy to understand why many people are confused about physical fitness. To some, having a high level of physical fitness means being a good athlete. It is true that most athletes are in very good shape; however, you do not have to be an athlete to be physically fit.

BODY WEIGHT CAN BE MISLEADING

Today there seems to be a slimness mania, especially among females. Individuals with this attitude frequently measure physical fitness by the bathroom scale. If the scale indicates that the person weighs what she wants to weigh, she is happy. If, on the other hand, the scale indicates a reading that is five pounds over the desired weight, she is unhappy. This attitude is an unfortunate misconception about physical fitness. Being obese is certainly a factor that works against being physically fit, but many young people believe they are physically fit just because their weight is a desirable one. Do you know anyone who is slender yet in terrible physical condition? Appropriate weight is just one indication of physical fitness, but it is not the only indication that a person is physically fit.

The smile tells the story. It is obvious she likes what the scale says.

Some people have an obsession about being fat and, in struggling to control their weight, may deprive themselves of important nutrients. The myth that thinness means fitness has been promoted successfully by the various media. This course will help you take a closer look at the myths and fallacies that surround being physically fit.

PHYSICAL FITNESS DEFINED

As teenagers you are concerned with looking good and feeling good, so it is essential that you understand **physical fitness**. People are described as being physically fit when they are able to carry out daily tasks without undue fatigue, are able to handle emergency situations, and possess sufficient energy to enjoy leisure time pursuits. Physical fitness is determined by the condition of your heart and circulatory system, respiratory system, muscular system, degree of flexibility, and percentage of body fat.

PRIMARY HEALTH RISK FACTORS

You can significantly change the current state of your health, as well as the state of your future health, by controlling **primary health risk factors** associated with disease, disability, or premature death. The removal of even one of these risk factors may reduce the threat of several diseases. Although you may think these risk factors are relevant only to older people, those your parent's age for example, they are relevant to you as well. Since many of these diseases start when a person is a teenager or even younger, it is to your benefit to learn how you can control these factors. The most commonly identified risk factors are discussed below.

INACTIVITY

Those who remain active have fewer heart problems and other diseases than those who remain inactive. **Inactivity** limits your chance of being in charge of your life because physical health is important to your total development. Being physically active helps you feel good about yourself.

BOY, THIS IS THE LIFE!

How much time do you sit watching television?

OBESITY

Having excessive deposits of fat in the body is called **obesity**. These fatty deposits put a strain on your heart and circulatory system, as well as on all other systems of your body. It has also been reported that obese individuals may have a hard time adjusting socially and emotionally. Obesity, or the initial stages of obesity, begin in childhood. Many young people are unable to control this condition during their school years and, therefore, end up as obese adults.

HIGH BLOOD PRESSURE

This condition has been identified as a major cause of heart and other circulatory problems. You may know people, your parents or their friends, who have **high blood pressure**. It is important to understand that high blood pressure does not occur just in older people. Many people your age have high blood pressure, caused by the stresses of home life, school work, and peer pressure.

HIGH LEVELS OF CHOLESTEROL

Cholesterol is a waxy, fatlike substance found in the cells. Although cholesterol is needed by the body, diets high in saturated fat can cause cholesterol levels to become too high. When this occurs, the cholesterol may collect in blood vessels and clog them. This is why high levels of cholesterol in the blood frequently are associated with heart disease.

The average American consumes a diet extremely high in fat content. While foods at fast-food restaurants are very tasty, they are generally very high in fat and, therefore, can increase your cholesterol level.

STRESS AND TENSION

Unnecessary stress and tension may place a strain on the heart and circulatory system and may lead to various types of diseases. An argument with a close friend may cause you to experience unusual anger, doubt, or fear which in turn can have a negative effect on your body. Who has not been upset at a parent, teacher, or friend? What happened to your body? Was it "revved up," or ready for action, as evidenced by a rapid heart beat and rapid rate of breathing? The teen years are a very challenging time. In fact, the early teens may be the most difficult time in the lives of many people.

Who said teenagers' lives were easy?

SMOKING

You have undoubtedly heard about the negative health effects of smoking on your body. It has been firmly established that smoking causes many problems in the circulatory and respiratory systems of your body. The Federal Drug Administration has declared the nicotine contained in tobacco to be addictive. It is a widely known fact that trying to stop smoking, after it has become a habit, is very difficult. You may know individuals who have found it very hard to break the habit. However, you are 100 percent in control of this risk factor if you never start.

SEX OF INDIVIDUAL

In the past, men have had higher rates of heart disease than women. The primary reason was that men were more affected by the pressures and stresses of the business world. However, the gap appears to be narrowing since more women have entered the work force and experienced the same pressures and tensions. The increased number of women who smoke may also be a factor in the increased rate of heart disease among women.

HEREDITY

If you have family members who have had heart attacks or other circulatory problems, your chances of having heart problems increase. In other words, you not only inherit your parents' and grandparents' physical characteristics, but you also tend to develop the same diseases they had.

AGE

Advancing age increases the risk of developing coronary heart disease. This is easily understood when one considers that the collection of arterial plaque is an ongoing process and the longer one lives, the greater the build-up.

Six of the nine health risk factors can be controlled. Are you a good lion tamer in your own life?

While it is true the risk of heart disease increases as one gets older, steps can be taken now to reduce the rate of increase. For example, just because you get older does not mean you should become inactive, nor does it give you an excuse for gaining excessive amounts of weight.

CONTRIBUTING HEALTH RISK FACTOR

A contributing health risk factor not as important as smoking or high blood pressure, is **diabetes**. However, the American Heart Association considers diabetes a contributing risk factor that should not be ignored. **Diabetes** is the inability of the body to produce or use insulin. Insulin is necessary for the body to utilize glucose (sugar).

Without insulin, glucose absorption by the cells and liver is low, leading to high glucose levels in the blood. It is estimated that 80 percent of diabetics die with some form of heart or blood vessel disease. Changes in eating habits, weight control, exercise habits, and drug therapy are often used to keep diabetes under control.

BENEFITS OF EXERCISE

What's in it for you? The answer to this question is highly personal. For example, everyone benefits from physical activity, however, we all place different importance on the various benefits. While some of the benefits may not be meaningful to you now, they may be to others or may become meaningful to you latter in life.

IMPROVED APPEARANCE

Looking good is very important to everyone, particularly to students your age. Exercise and fitness activities help control body weight and help make your body more attractive. Music stars and other performers are very concerned about their appearance and consequently follow well-designed fitness programs. Physical activity helps to tone muscles and shape the body.

If you improve your personal physical appearance, there is a likelihood you will also improve the way you feel about yourself in an overall sense. This improvement may create a positive change in your life. As you improve your physical appearance, your feelings about yourself improve. When you feel good about yourself, the chances are greater that you will want to continue to improve yourself, not just in a physical way but in every way.

Both young men and women can benefit from muscular strength and endurance exercises.

IMPROVED BODY IMAGE

Body image means the way you see your physical self. Are you pleased when you look in a full length mirror? Since many people do not like their body images, properly designed physical fitness programs may be the answer for them. Remember, your body image is just one part of your self-concept. Improving your body image can also improve the total way you see and feel about yourself.

Do you like what you see in the mirror? Is the mirror a friend or foe?

IMPROVED SELF-CONTROL

People who take control of their bodies and their lifestyles generally experience less stress and depression than those who are indifferent about personal improvement. Having control of these aspects of your life may also help you have greater feelings of self-confidence, regardless of the situations in which you find yourself.

MORE ENJOYMENT OF LIFE

While many people your age enjoy life, there are many more who, for one reason or another, have a lot of pressure and stress in their lives. Physical activity can provide not only relief from daily anxieties, but also can have a refreshing, exhilarating effect on your life.

IMPROVED HEALTH

Physical activity beyond the daily routine is needed to avoid heart disease and other illnesses associated with inactivity. This is especially true for older people, but it also has relevance for you. Active people are healthier because their digestion is enhanced through exercise, providing better elimination of waste products from the body.

INCREASED MUSCULAR STRENGTH AND ENDURANCE

The vast majority of male teenagers are anxious to be as strong as possible and to have well-developed muscles. While the majority of female teenagers do not want to develop large muscles, they do want to have firm, well-toned bodies. In both cases, the end result of a physical fitness program will be improved personal appearance and self-confidence. This leads directly to the next benefit of physical fitness.

Is your body as important as a car? Do you know people who take better care of their cars than they do of their bodies?

INCREASED LEVEL OF ENERGY

Being tired during the day may be the direct result of lifestyle choices like poor nutritional and rest habits. Low energy may also be due to a body that is not tuned-up appropriately. Your body could be compared to an expensive car. Do you know anyone who would put low octane gas in a fancy sports car or disregard all professional advice for handling it?

Our bodies are much more valuable than the most expensive cars, yet it is strange that we sometimes disregard recommended guidelines for getting the maximum performance from them. Appropriate physical activities are key factors in helping your body function near an optimal level. A higher energy level is one outcome of following a physical fitness program. A high level of physical activity will prevent fatigue and allow you to enjoy leisure activities to a greater degree.

IMPROVED PHYSICAL PERFORMANCE

If you are physically fit, you will not fatigue as quickly and therefore will be able to play longer, gain more skill, and experience a greater degree of success and enjoyment in games and sports. You will also be able to complete your school day with little fatigue.

Someone once said, "Fatigue makes cowards of us all." Whether or not this is a true statement is unimportant. The point to be kept in mind is that fatigue or a low energy level keeps you from performing near your best level.

INCREASED SUCCESS IN YOUR SCHOOL WORK OR JOB

Ancient Greeks used a phrase that summed up their belief about the importance of the body: **a sound mind in a sound body.** They thought this phrase was essential in the education of children. Research studies show that increased physical fitness helps increase academic achievement. As your body becomes more efficient, you function more effectively.

HELPS COPE WITH STRESS

Teenagers are under many stresses today and frequently become depressed, angry, or anxious about their lives. A good exercise program can be one of the most important ways to deal with stress. In Chapter 11, you will learn several easy techniques for recognizing and handling the stress in your life.

Improved physical fitness helps to ward off fatigue.

SLEEP BETTER

For the majority of you, sleeping may not be a problem. However, this is not true for everyone. Exercise relieves tension, and so your body relaxes more, enabling you to go to sleep quickly and to sleep soundly.

INCREASED LIFE EXPECTANCY

This benefit may seem to be more related to your parents or older friends than to you. Remember the comparison of your body to an expensive car? A car motor will last much longer if it is cared for properly, and so will your body. Many diseases attributed to inactivity begin at an early age because individuals disregard the needs of their bodies and abuse them.

Physical fitness activities provide almost immediate physical and mental benefits. The physical benefits include looking good and feeling good about yourself. The mental benefits include increased self-esteem, improved self-control, and a feeling of confidence.

 Can you think of other benefits? The important point to remember is that there are many benefits of exercise for everyone, especially for high school students.

YOU HAVE A CHOICE!

SUMMARY

There is no easy path to being physically fit and healthy. Some would like us to believe there is because they make millions of dollars from our purchases. It is a fantasy to think you can take a pill, or do a two-minute-a-day exercise and become fit. If you wish to gain, regain, or maintain a high level of personal physical well-being, you must be prepared to give time and effort to attain your goal.

To be successful at this goal, you need to answer the following questions honestly:

1. Are you satisfied with your present state of physical fitness?
2. Are you satisfied with your body image (what the mirror shows)?
3. Does your lifestyle include vigorous physical activity?
4. Are you satisfied with your present lifestyle?

If you answered no to any of these questions, you should recognize the need for engaging in a personal fitness program. **The challenge is yours. Go for it.**

TRUE-FALSE

Circle "T" for all correct statements and "F" for all incorrect ones.

T F 1. Setting up a personal physical fitness program may provide both physical and mental benefits.

T F 2. The way people look has little effect on how they feel about themselves.

T F 3. During the past 15 years, there has been a remarkable increase of interest in physical fitness.

T F 4. Teenagers are less concerned about their appearance than older people.

T F 5. The media is one reason some people have negative attitudes toward their own bodies.

T F 6. A person does not need to be an athlete to be very healthy and physically active.

T F 7. Physical fitness deals with five factors: cardiovascular fitness, muscular strength, muscular endurance, flexibility, and body composition.

T F 8. Body image refers to the way you see your physical self.

T F 9. Improving physical fitness has nothing to do with ones energy level.

T F 10. Taking control of your body and lifestyle may help you experience less stress and depression.

RISK FACTOR CHECKLIST

Check the appropriate column for each risk factor.

		I CAN CONTROL	I CANNOT CONTROL
11.	INACTIVITY	✓	
12.	OBESITY		
13.	HIGH BLOOD PRESSURE		
14.	HIGH LEVELS OF CHOLESTEROL		
15.	STRESS AND TENSION		
16.	SMOKING		
17.	SEX OF INDIVIDUAL		
18.	HEREDITY		
19.	AGE		

DISCUSSION

20. In what way is physical fitness related to body image?

21. What effect can advertisements have on the way people see themselves physically?

22. Why is the word *personal* so important in a personal fitness class?

23. Compare two people, one who is fit and one who is unfit. Are there any differences in them besides the amount of physical activity in their lives?

24. What is the relationship, if any, between body image and self-esteem?

COMPONENTS OF FITNESS

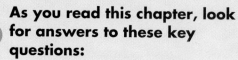

CHAPTER OBJECTIVES

As you read this chapter, look for answers to these key questions:

- What is the difference between health-related and skill-related physical fitness?

- What are the health-related components of physical fitness?

- What are the skill-related components of physical fitness?

- Why does a person not have to be a good athlete to be physically fit?

- Why is it important to know your current level of health-related fitness?

VOCABULARY

When you have completed this chapter, you should understand the meaning of these vocabulary terms:

- skill-related fitness
- health-related fitness
- flexibility
- cardiovascular fitness
- muscular strength
- muscular endurance
- body composition
- agility
- balance
- power
- reaction time
- coordination
- speed
- norm-referenced tests
- criterion-referenced tests
- health-related fitness standards

If it is to be, it is up to me.

ANALYZING PHYSICAL FITNESS

There has been a lot of confusion centered on the answers to these questions: What is physical fitness? How can it be attained? It is very important that you understand the answers to these questions if you are going to become responsible for your own health and fitness.

Physical fitness is made up of both health-related and skill-related components. The **skill-related fitness** items relate to the possibility of you becoming a good athlete. Are you fast? Do you have good eye–hand coordination? The **health-related fitness** components relate to how well the systems of your body operate. Are your heart and other muscles in good shape? This type of physical fitness is related to your overall state of health. The focus of this book is on the health-related components of physical fitness— why they are important and how they can be improved.

Both kinds of fitness are important to successful participation in sports activities. However, only the health-related components, if adequately developed, can contribute to the prevention of disease and the promotion of health. That is why they are called health-related.

Maintaining an acceptable level of the health-related components of physical fitness is recognized as a key element of a healthy lifestyle. People who attain such levels of fitness reduce their risks of developing health problems, such as heart disease, low back pain, and obesity, and improve their body's ability to function. This is why health-related fitness should be the concern of everyone.

There are five health-related components of physical fitness: flexibility, cardiovascular fitness, muscular strength, muscular endurance, and body composition. Remember that fitness is for everyone. You do not have to be a good athlete to be physically fit. If you exercise regularly and follow basic training principles, you will improve your health-related fitness.

FLEXIBILITY

Flexibility describes the range of movement possible at various joints. It is probably the most frequently overlooked component of fitness. You can get along without being flexible only if you

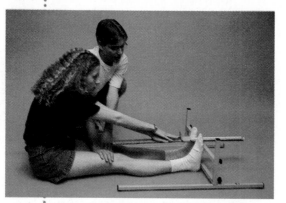

The sit-and-reach test measures flexibility.

are inactive and do not wish to operate near your maximum capacity. If you want to be as good as you can be, you must work on flexibility as regularly as you work on muscular strength and endurance or cardiovascular efficiency.

Because flexibility is specific to each joint, no single test can provide complete information about the flexibility of all major joints of your body. However, there are several tests that will give you an indication of flexibility in joints most likely needing attention. These tests include the sit-and-reach test, the shoulder lift test, and the broomstick dynamic flexibility test. Flexibility of your lower back and posterior thighs can be evaluated using the sit-and-reach test.

Sit-and-Reach Test

Procedures:

1. Warm up prior to testing.

2. Remove your shoes and sit at the test box with your legs fully extended.

3. Place your feet shoulder width apart, flat against the test box.

4. Slide your arms forward with palms down and one hand on top of the other.

5. As a partner gently places his or her hands on your knees to keep them from bending, reach forward, sliding your fingertips as far forward along the ruler as possible and hold that position for one second. Do not bounce or rock forward.

6. Have your partner measure the distance your fingertips reach to the nearest centimeter.

7. Allow four trials and record the best reach.

CARDIOVASCULAR FITNESS

Cardiovascular fitness relates to the ability of the heart, blood, blood vessels, and the respiratory system to supply oxygen and necessary fuel to the muscles during exercise. The best type of exercise for improving cardiovascular fitness is aerobic exercise. Aerobic exercises are those activities which force the body to use a large amount of oxygen for a sustained period of time. Sustained means that the exercise should be done for a period of 15 to 30 minutes to get the aerobic benefits. Examples of aerobic exercises are jogging, cycling, swimming, rope jumping, and aerobic dance.

You may run for distance or time to measure aerobic endurance.

Certain sports, like basketball and soccer, also provide the workout needed to achieve an aerobic training effect. Aerobic exercise provides a safeguard for your physical and mental health.

Cardiovascular fitness can be measured in a number of ways. The most accurate measurement is a stress test performed on a stationary bicycle or treadmill in a physical fitness laboratory or hospital. This test requires expensive equipment and highly trained personnel. Cardiovascular fitness can be more easily evaluated with step tests and distance runs. The most common distance runs are the one-mile run and the one-and-a-half-mile run for time and the nine-minute run and the twelve-minute run for distance. Prior to performing a distance run, you should practice running to learn how to pace yourself. It is also important to condition yourself before attempting a timed run.

One-Mile Run

Procedures:

1. Warm up prior to testing.
2. Start the timer and cover the one-mile distance as fast as possible.
3. Use the fastest pace that you can sustain for the entire one-mile distance.
4. Walk if you have to; however, your goal is to cover the one-mile in the shortest time possible.
5. After you have covered the one-mile, stop the timer and record the time (minutes and seconds) it took you to cover this distance.
6. Cool down after testing.

MUSCULAR STRENGTH AND MUSCULAR ENDURANCE

Muscular strength and endurance are closely related components very important to teenagers. **Muscular strength** is the ability of a muscle group to apply a maximal force against a resistance one time. **Muscular endurance** is the ability to repeat muscle movement for a long period of time.

In the past, young men were much more interested in muscular development than young women were. That gap is closing rapidly as more women are realizing the importance of developing their muscular fitness. Today, more than ever before, women want to have firm and well-toned bodies. An important fact to remember is that most females will not develop large muscles for the simple reason that they do not have enough of the necessary hormone

Sit-ups and crunches measure abdominal muscular strength and endurance.

testosterone. Males, on the other hand, have a high level of the male hormone (testosterone), enabling them to greatly increase muscle size and body definition. Regardless of whether you are male or female, improving your muscular development will improve your body image.

Abdominal muscular strength and endurance can be easily measured by performance of sit-ups for a one-minute time period. Pull-ups, chin-ups, flexed-arm hang, push-ups, and parallel bar dips are commonly used to evaluate muscular strength and endurance of the upper body.

Sit-Up Test

Procedures:

1. Stretch the abdominal muscles prior to testing.
2. Lie flat on your back with your knees bent, feet on the floor, and heels 12 to 18 inches from your buttocks.
3. Cross your arms, and place them across your chest with your hands on opposite shoulders.
4. Have your partner hold your feet to keep them in contact with the floor.
5. Curl up to a sitting position, keeping your arms in contact with your chest. A sit-up is completed when your elbows touch your thighs. Return to the down position by uncurling until your midback makes contact with the floor.
6. Perform as many sit-ups as you can in one minute.
7. Stretch the abdominal muscles after testing.

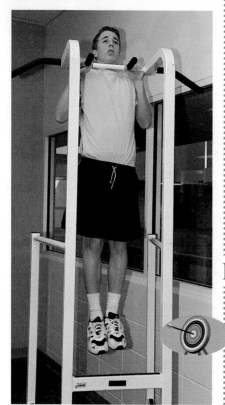

Pull-ups measure upper body muscular strength and endurance.

BODY COMPOSITION

Body composition is the ratio of fat to muscle, bone, and other tissues that compose your body. A certain amount of body fat is needed for good health. Extremely high or low amounts of body fat can cause health problems. Most young adults desire a low percent of body fat. Your **body image** may suffer if your percent of body fat is too high. Looking good and feeling good depends a great deal on what percent of your body weight is fat. The information in this text, if put to use, will help you achieve an ideal body weight and an appropriate level of body fat.

Body composition can be evaluated in several ways. Underwater weighing is the most accurate method of determining what percent of body weight is fat. However, this method requires expensive equipment and trained personnel. Body composition is more commonly assessed by measuring the thickness of skinfolds, using a device called a skinfold caliper. Triceps and calf skinfold measurements provide a good estimate of the percent of body weight that is fat.

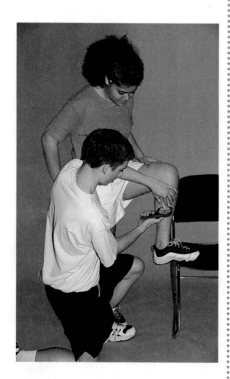

Triceps and calf skinfold measurements assess body composition.

Tricep and Calf Skinfolds

Procedures:

1. Have your partner mark the following sites with a marking pencil:

    triceps—midpoint between your shoulder and your elbow on the back of your right arm

    calf—inside your right lower leg at the largest part of your calf

2. When measuring your triceps skinfold, stand erect with your right arm relaxed.

3. When measuring your calf skinfold, place your right foot on an elevated surface, or sit in a chair so that your knee is bent at a 90-degree angle.

4. Have your partner take the measurements by pinching a fold of your skin between the thumb and forefinger slightly above the mark. Have your partner measure the thickness of the skinfold at the mark by pulling the fold away from the underlying muscle and applying the skinfold caliper to the fold.

5. Have your partner take three consecutive measurements at each site. Read the skinfold to the nearest millimeter. Disregard the highest and lowest reading and record the middle measurement.

6. Add the middle measurement of your three triceps measurements to the middle measurement of your three calf measurements.

7. Using the sum obtained in #6, follow the directions in Activity 10-2 in the Student Activity Handbook or directions provided by your teacher to deteremine your percentage of body fat.

SKILL-RELATED FITNESS

There are six skill-related components of physical fitness: agility, balance, power, reaction time, coordination, and speed. These factors contribute to your ability to successfully participate in sports activities. Regular participation in sports or other recreational pursuits can have a positive influence on your health and fitness. Individuals who have a high level of skill-related fitness are more likely to be physically active than those who have a lower level of skill.

AGILITY

Agility is the ability to change the position of your body and to control the movement of your whole body. Agility is an important quality in many sports, because you must change direction rapidly and always have your body under control.

Agility tests are similar to conditioning and practice drills used in various sports. Shuttle runs, zigzag runs, and the hexagonal jump are some examples of ways to measure agility.

The zigzag run may be used to measure agility.

BALANCE

Balance is the ability to keep an upright posture while either standing still or moving. Good balance is essential to be successful in activities such as ice skating, skiing, surfing, and gymnastics.

Many challenging tasks can be used to evaluate balance. Some examples are standing as long as possible on the ball of one foot, standing as long as possible on a balance board or roller board with one foot or both feet, walking on a balance beam, and doing headstands and handstands.

Standing on one foot can be used to measure static balance. Walking on a balance beam is used to measure dynamic balance.

POWER

Power is the ability to perform with strength at a rapid pace. Strength and speed are both involved in power. Football players, swimmers, shot-putters, discus throwers, and high jumpers are examples of athletes who typically have a high degree of power.

The vertical jump can be used to measure power.

The vertical jump and the standing long jump are commonly used to assess power.

REACTION TIME

Reaction time is the amount of time it takes to start a movement once your senses signal the need to move. People with good reaction time can usually start quickly in track and swimming or react quickly in ping pong or karate.

A very simple assessment of reaction time is the yardstick test. The object of this test is to catch the yardstick as quickly as possible when it starts to fall. Scoring is based on how far the yardstick falls before you catch it.

COORDINATION

Coordination is the integration of eye, hand, and foot movements. This component is necessary for success in such sports as tennis, golf, and basketball, where good hand–eye coordination is essential.

Like agility, tests of coordination are similar to conditioning and practice drills used in various sports. Some examples are dribbling and shooting in basketball, place kicking and punting in football, and dribbling in soccer.

A yardstick may be used to measure reaction time.

A ball toss against a wall can be used to measure hand-eye coordination.

Kicking a soccer ball against a wall can be used to measure foot-eye coordination.

SPEED

Speed is the ability to cover a distance in a short time. Speed is a very important factor in many sports activities.

Short runs are used to evaluate speed. Examples of such tests are the 50-yard dash and the 100-yard dash. The 40-yard dash is the most frequently used measure of speed in football.

The 50-yard dash can be used to measure speed.

FITNESS ASSESSMENT

Before beginning a personal fitness program, you should know your present level of flexibility, cardiovascular fitness, muscular strength and endurance, and body composition. You should also know how to assess each of these components and how to interpret the results. The health-related fitness tests described in the **Personal Fitness: Looking Good/Feeling Good Student Activity Handbook** will help you learn how to measure your own fitness level, identify your strengths and weaknesses, and interpret your test results. The first assessment, or pre-test, will help you determine your present fitness level and provide you with a basis for setting realistic goals. The post-test, at the conclusion of the instructional program, will help you determine the progress you made toward your goals and assist you in setting new goals.

IMPORTANCE OF SELF-TESTING

Periodic self-testing is an effective way to monitor your progress, determine the effectiveness of your personal fitness program, and re-evaluate and update your goals. This is why it is important for you to be able to assess yourself and interpret the results. You are encouraged to test yourself anytime you wish to check your progress. Self-testing enables you to determine when and how much to change your personal fitness program. It also allows you to check your progress toward your desired level of health-related fitness. By repeating the tests from time to time, you will develop a sense of your personal fitness needs and the ability to solve your own fitness problems.

INTERPRETING ASSESSMENT RESULTS

Some physical fitness tests utilize norms to indicate fitness levels. These are called **norm-referenced tests**. Assessment results are indicated in percentile rankings. Percentile rankings represent the percentage of individuals of the same age and sex who scored at or below your test score. If, for example, you performed at the 75th percentile, you achieved a score better than 75 percent of those in your age group. Percentile rankings, however, should only be used as an indication of your strengths and weaknesses, not as a means of comparing yourself to other people. Remember that fitness is a personal matter. Compete with yourself, not with others.

Percentile Norms for the Mile Run (minutes and seconds)					
Females					
Age	13	14	15	16	17+
Percentile					
95	7:12	7:20	7:41	7:09	7:30
75	8:20	8:15	8:44	9:02	9:05
50	9:29	9:37	10:07	10:47	9:49
25	10:58	11:45	12:23	13:02	11:30
5	14:57	17:01	16:24	15:32	15:26
Males					
Age	13	14	15	16	17+
Percentile					
95	6:13	5:53	6:03	5:50	6:03
75	6:54	6:38	6:37	6:30	6:38
50	7:29	7:12	7:16	7:13	7:27
25	8:37	8:04	8:06	8:09	8:28
5	10:25	10:34	10:39	10:42	11:00

Other physical fitness tests use specific standards to judge fitness levels. These are called **criterion-referenced tests**. **Health-**

related fitness standards represent satisfactory levels of flexibility, cardiovascular fitness, muscular strength and endurance, and body composition necessary for good health. Achieving these standards is important to good health. Not only will you be less susceptible to various health problems if you attain these standards, but you will also be more likely to feel and look good.

Health-Fitness Standards for the Mile Run (minutes and seconds)		
Age	Females	Males
13	11:00	8:30
14	10:30	8:15
15	10:30	8:00
16	10:30	8:00
17	10:30	8:00
18	10:30	8:00

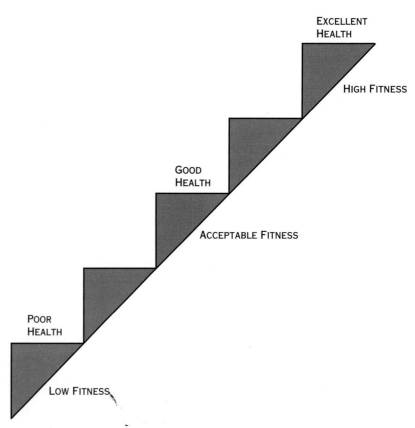

Achieving acceptable health-related fitness standards is important to good health.

GOAL SETTING

In Chapter 3 you will learn about the importance of goal setting in relation to health and fitness. When you develop your goals, it is essential that you utilize the information regarding your present level of fitness. That is the purpose of the pre-test.

It is important to remember that individuals will improve at different rates. If you score far below the health-related fitness standard in a particular component, you have the potential to make enormous progress in that area. If you score near, at, or above the standard, you may improve only moderately. The more fit you are, the harder you will have to work to make small gains. Less fit individuals may show dramatic improvement, yet remain far below their potential. The important thing is to do the best you can. Remember that fitness is for everyone.

SUMMARY

There are two kinds of physical fitness: health-related fitness and skill-related fitness. The health-related fitness components are essential to a healthy lifestyle and the prevention of health problems. That is why they are called health-related. The five health-related fitness components are flexibility, cardiovascular fitness, muscular strength, muscular endurance, and body composition.

The skill-related fitness components are concerned with abilities related to sports activities. They include agility, balance, power, reaction time, coordination, and speed.

There are several tests to measure each component of physical fitness. Knowledge of how to conduct these tests will allow you to determine your fitness level throughout life. Some physical fitness test results are indicated in percentile rankings and are called norm-referenced tests. Others use specific standards to judge your fitness status and are called criterion-referenced tests.

Before beginning a personal fitness program, you should know your present level of health-related fitness in order to set realistic goals. Self-testing is an effective way to monitor your program. This is why it is crucial that you know how to evaluate yourself and interpret the results.

Physical fitness is for everyone. You do not have to be a good athlete to be physically fit. If you exercise regularly and follow basic training principles, you will improve your health-related fitness.

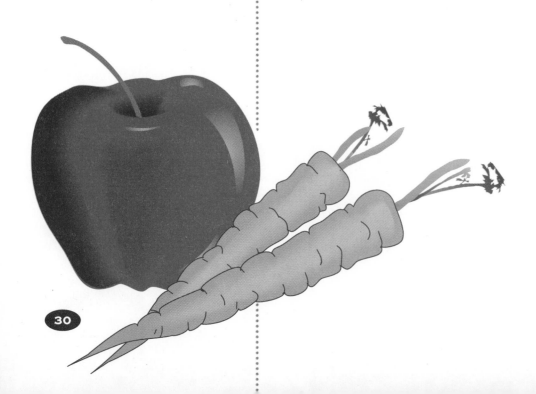

STUDY QUESTIONS

VOCABULARY MATCHING

Place the letter of the correct answer in the space provided.

.... 1. Cardiovascular fitness

.... 2. Aerobic exercises

.... 3. Health-related fitness components

.... 4. Skill-related fitness components

.... 5. Muscular strength and endurance

.... 6. Flexibility

.... 7. Body composition

.... 8. Agility

.... 9. Power

.... 10. Reaction time

.... 11. Coordination

.... 12. Speed

A. Range of movement possible at various joints

B. Factors related to becoming stronger

C. Factors related to becoming a better athlete

D. Ratio of fat to muscle, bone, and other tissue

E. Ability to change the position of your body and control the movement of your body

F. Ability to cover a distance in a short time

G. Integration of eye, hand, and foot movements

H. Amount of time it takes to get moving

I. Ability to do strength performances at a rapid pace

J. Factors related to how well the systems of your body work

K. Activities which force the body to use a large amount of oxygen for an extended period of time

L. Ability of the circulatory and respiratory systems to supply oxygen to muscles during exercise

FITNESS COMPONENT CHECKLIST

Listed below are the components of physical fitness. In the space provided, indicate whether the component is a health-related (HR) or a skill-related (SR) component.

13. .... Balance

14. .... Body composition

15. .... Coordination

16. .... Speed

17. .... Muscular strength

18. .... Muscular endurance

19. .... Power

20. .... Flexibility

21. .... Reaction time

22. .... Cardiovascular fitness

23. .... Agility

DISCUSSION

24. What is the difference between health-related fitness and skill-related fitness?

25. Why should everyone be concerned about health-related fitness?

26. What are some tests for assessing each of the health-related components of fitness?

27. Why is it important to know how to assess your own physical fitness level?

28. Describe the difference between norm-referenced tests and criterion-referenced tests.

GOAL SETTING FOR TEENAGERS

3

CHAPTER OBJECTIVES

As you read this chapter, look for answers to these key questions:

- What are goals?

- What is goal setting?

- How can setting goals help you take control of your health and fitness?

- What is the difference between long-term goals and short-term goals?

- What are the steps necessary for successful goal setting?

VOCABULARY

When you have completed this chapter, you should understand the meaning of these vocabulary terms:

- goal setting
- long-term goal
- short-term goal
- time line

> **Nothing can stop people with the right mental attitude from achieving their goals.**
>
> THOMAS JEFFERSON

TEEN YEARS: A TOPSY-TURVY TIME

The term *topsy-turvy* means that things are not very certain or in disorder. That is why the term seems appropriate to teenage life. As a teenager, you may disagree with this point because you are one of the lucky people who are happy with their lives. However, it is true that many teenagers find this period of time confusing and frustrating. As a teen, you are in transition from childhood to adulthood. During this transition you experience physical, social, emotional and mental changes. These changes can create positive or negative experiences. The positive experiences include physical maturation, a sense of independence,

the discovery of new abilities, and the satisfaction of taking care of yourself. The negative changes include unusual physical differences between peers, moodiness, self-consciousness, discovery of personal limitations, and difficulties involved in taking on new responsibilities.

Teen years bring about both good and not-so-good feelings caused by changes in a person's physical, social, emotional, and mental being.

While the teen years are an emotionally unsettled time, they can also be a fantastic time for learning how to take more control of your own life. Up until this time in your life, your parents have been making most of the decisions about what you eat, what you wear, where you go, who your friends are, and in which activities you are involved. Now you must take more responsibility in making these decisions. Of course, you will still need guidance from your parents and teachers to help you refine your decision-making ability.

TAKING CONTROL OF YOUR HEALTH AND FITNESS

Now that you are starting to have more control over your own life, you need to accept responsibility for it. Two aspects of your life that need a tremendous amount of attention are your health and fitness. Making responsible decisions about diet, exercise, and the use of your time will have an impact on your lifestyle. As you know, your body image has a direct effect on how you feel about yourself. Learning to make appropriate decisions about your personal program of health and fitness is essential to becoming happy and successful.

Do you have friends who would like to be stronger, weigh more, weigh less, or play sports? Undoubtedly you do. If they want these things, why don't they have them? Unfortunately, there is a big gap between wanting something in life and making it happen. Wouldn't it be nice to wish for something and have it happen? Who wouldn't like a money tree in the backyard? Owning a money tree is a wish, not a realistic goal. A realistic goal of having more spending money takes more than a wish; it requires effort on your part.

Goal setting must begin with realistic ideas.

One major reason that people are often not as healthy and active as they desire to be is that they have never been taught how to set goals. This personal fitness course is a good start in the right direction, but the responsibility for making proper decisions about your own health and physical fitness is yours. This chapter will discuss goal setting as a means of helping you realize more of your potential.

WHAT ARE GOALS?

I'M READY FOR THE CHALLENGE OF IMPROVING MYSELF, AND I'M STARTING TODAY!

Goals help you take control of your life.

Almost anything you desire can be a goal. Buying a car, getting better grades, changing your body weight, getting stronger, getting a date with a certain person, or making the track team are personal goals. Goals serve as a guide for what you do and give you something to work toward. Setting personal goals helps you do your best and achieve what you want in life.

In this course, the focus is on health-related fitness. Therefore, you will be encouraged to set goals in flexibility, cardiovascular fitness, muscular strength and endurance, and body composition. You will also be encouraged to set health-related goals in nutrition, weight control, and stress management.

WHAT IS GOAL SETTING?

Goal setting is a process that can help you improve yourself and, therefore, feel good about yourself. It is a means of getting you motivated about self-improvement and lifestyle. The following sections on long-term goals, short-term goals, and the steps involved in the goal setting process will help you understand goal setting. It is not a difficult process, but it will take effort and commitment on your part.

LONG-TERM GOALS

Although you may not realize it, you probably set goals all the time. Some of your goals may take a long time to reach, perhaps years. An example of a **long-term goal** would be to go to college and study to become a doctor or computer programmer. Another long-term goal would be to save money to buy a car. But long-term goals do not have to take years. You may want to accomplish the goal of becoming a leader in student government, during this semester; that would also be a long-term goal. None of these examples can be achieved in a short period of time. But all can be achieved with the use of short-term goals.

SHORT-TERM GOALS

Short-term goals are goals that can be established either to help you achieve a long-term goal or help you accomplish something in a short period of time. Short-term goals can be reached in a few days or weeks. Short-term goals are usually specific, while long-term goals are more general. Examples of some short-term goals include studying hard to get a good grade on next week's algebra test or earning enough money to buy concert tickets for this coming weekend.

GOAL SETTING IS LIKE A LADDER

LONG TERM GOAL

–10 POUNDS	WEEK 10
–9 POUNDS	WEEK 9
–8 POUNDS	WEEK 8
–7 POUNDS	WEEK 7
–6 POUNDS	WEEK 6
–5 POUNDS	WEEK 5
–4 POUNDS	WEEK 4
–3 POUNDS	WEEK 3
–2 POUNDS	WEEK 2
–1 POUNDS	WEEK 1

Use short-term goals to reach a long-term goal.

The establishment of goals can be compared to a ladder. Think of the top rung of a ladder as your long-term goal and the rungs leading to it as your short-term goals. Each rung (short-term goal) you climb will put you in a better position to reach your long-term goal. Notice how the ladder in the drawing illustrates this analogy. In this situation, the person wants to lose ten pounds—the long-term goal represented by the top rung on the ladder. Instead of just setting a long-term goal of losing ten pounds, which is difficult for many people, this person set ten short-term goals of losing one pound per week, represented by each of the ten rungs of the ladder. It is important for anyone who is just beginning to set goals to start by setting short-term goals. These goals should not be too difficult to achieve, and you will feel good when you've reached each one. Reaching one rung can act as a motivation to encourage you to reach the next rung (short-term goal) on the ladder. By setting goals using the ladder method, you will see concrete progress and develop a sense of confidence. An increased feeling of self-confidence can inspire you to want to reach for higher rungs on your performance ladder.

GOAL-SETTING STEPS

The following information on how to set personal goals will be of value to you only if you sincerely wish to make changes in your lifestyle.

DESIRE

Desire is the most important factor in goal setting. Wanting to improve yourself in some way is essential before you can start setting goals. Goals are personal. Parents, friends, or teachers cannot set goals for you. It is completely up to you. Other people can help you only after you have decided how you want to change. In what ways would you like to improve yourself?

BELIEF

Wanting to make a change and making it are two different things. You undoubtedly know people who want to stop smoking or lose 15 pounds but never do it. Why do you suppose this is the case? In all probability they simply do not believe they can do it. An important point to remember is that if you believe you cannot do something, you probably can't. On the other hand, if you really believe you can do something, you have a better chance of accomplishing it. Want power can become will power.

ANALYZE WHERE YOU ARE NOW

Knowing your starting point is essential to establish both short-term and long-term goals. For example, if you wish to lose ten pounds, you need to know exactly what you weigh now. Or if you want to improve your diet, it is important to know what you currently eat over a two- or three-day period of time. Recording everything you eat and drink provides valuable information needed to identify the steps to be taken for improvement to occur. You may have already taken a pre-test on your physical fitness level. If you have, you know what your starting points are in regard to your flexibility, cardiovascular efficiency, muscular strength and endurance, and body composition.

SET REALISTIC GOALS

It is important for you to set goals that are realistic. A realistic goal is one you can reach. If your goals are too hard to reach, you may become discouraged and give up. If they are too easy, you may lose interest in them. Try to set goals that will stretch you and move you out of your comfort zone.

Accomplishing something that has pushed your mental strength to a new level will make you feel good about yourself and prepare you to reach for higher goals. Realistic goals are both reachable and challenging.

Realistic goal setting is based on your current level of physical fitness. For example, if you are only able to jog 440 yards without stopping, setting a goal of being able to jog a mile in 8 minutes in a month's time is probably unrealistic. A realistic goal for someone with this level of fitness may be to jog a mile in 12 minutes at the end of a month's time. In a four-month period of time, the individual may be able to jog one mile in 8 minutes. Similarly, if you can only do one pull-up, setting a goal of 10 additional pull-ups in a month's time may be unrealistic. On the other hand, setting a goal of 3 pull-ups in a month's time is realistic. Over a longer period of time, a goal of 10 pull-ups could be obtained and would be a realistic goal.

A winner is someone who has moved out of the "comfort zone." Such an individual has learned to set goals that are neither too hard nor too easy.

WRITE YOUR GOALS DOWN IN DETAIL

Putting your goals down on paper helps you to clarify what you want to do. When you think of something you want, it is just a wish. When you put it on paper, you are moving the idea along the road to success. Writing down your goals will allow you to get a clearer picture of what you want to do.

LIST BENEFITS YOU WILL RECEIVE

Identifying how you will benefit from accomplishing your goals is a very important step because the benefits you list will help make your desire stronger and, therefore, make your belief in yourself stronger. For example, if you wanted to begin a weight-lifting program so you will look better, which personal benefits would you list? The following are just a few of the benefits you would probably hope to gain.

a. improved body image

b. gain in energy

c. improved endurance

d. increased self-confidence and self-esteem

e. greater enjoyment of all types of physical activities

The more benefits you can list for accomplishing your goal, the greater will be your desire to make it happen. Remember the discussion in Chapter 1 about the benefits of being physically active?

Understanding the benefits of exercise will help motivate you to exercise.

IDENTIFY OBSTACLES

If you have never set goals before, you may not forsee the blocks or obstacles to attaining your goals. On the other hand, if you have tried to do something and failed, one obstacle may have been the doubt that you could really follow through and achieve your desired goal. Some obstacles may center on you, while other obstacles may center on your friends or your family. There is very little you cannot achieve in the areas of health and fitness if you have the willpower and belief in yourself. In your own life you are in the driver's seat and have the power to shape your lifestyle.

Obstacles are merely challenges for some people.

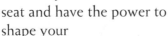

Attack obstacles you may face in your fitness program with confidence.

IDENTIFY KNOWLEDGE YOU WILL NEED

Wanting something and achieving it are two different things. If you want to reduce the stress in your life, you cannot wish it away. You will need to know how to reduce your stress before it can be actually reduced. This need for knowledge applies to any goal you set. Your physical education teacher will be able to help you gain the knowledge you need to reach your goals.

MAKE A PLAN OF ACTION

After all information has been collected, make a game plan; that is, outline a step-by-step strategy for accomplishing your goals. If your game plan is set up properly, you will experience success quickly and thus assure your continued progress toward attaining your goals.

DEVELOP A TIME LINE

While it is not easy to know exactly when you can accomplish your fitness goals, you may be able to get a pretty good idea, particularly if you seek advice from your physical education teacher. Setting **time lines** (times when something will be completed) is a simple and effective method to organize and plot your course to a major goal. Think of a physical fitness goal you would like to achieve this semester. For example, suppose you want to jog without stopping for 30 minutes by the end of the semester. The drawing of a time line shows how this can be done. Notice that while a time line does not provide you with the strategies to reach your long-term goal, it does set deadlines for making progress toward that goal.

Writing out your goals and putting them on a time line makes it easier to accomplish them. Using a time line:

a. gives you a better sense of control, organization, and direction

b. promotes greater commitment to your goals

c. helps relieve worry and confusion, especially as your individual deadlines approach

d. helps you pace your efforts

e. creates a sense of urgency to reach goals

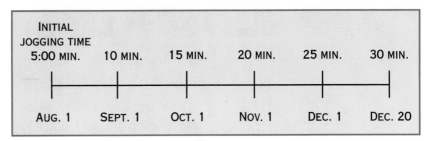

A time line helps you to pace your efforts toward reaching your goal.

Seeing your progress can help to keep you from losing interest in your goals.

MONITOR YOUR PROGRESS

Any goal setting should be accompanied by continuous monitoring to determine whether your goals are still reasonable. You may find that you need to readjust your short-term goals or even your long-term goals. A good monitoring process will keep you from wasting time or losing interest in your goal. Losing the belief that you can stick to your program is self-defeating. If this happens, get feedback from your parents, physical education teachers, or supportive friends.

NEVER GIVE UP

Back your plan with a determination that you will never give up. If you are just beginning to set goals, it could be very easy to give up. Do not be led astray by yourself or by others. Avoid sharing your goals with anyone who is not supportive. Be determined to take control of your lifestyle. Such determination will mean a lot to you.

GOAL SETTING IN ACTION

The following case study is an example of a course of action one high school student undertook to reach her goals.

Jodi was a 15-year-old tenth grader who did not feel comfortable in sports activities. Like most teenagers, she was concerned about looking as good as possible and feeling good about herself. Jodi was 5 feet 4 inches tall and weighed 128 pounds. When she took the physical fitness test at the beginning of the semester, she scored at the 25th percentile level in the mile run (12:21), and her percent of body fat was much higher than she wanted. Jodi did not like scoring so low in the mile-run or having such a high percent of body fat. One problem she had with her weight was the fact that some of her clothes were not fitting as well as they had a few months earlier. An even greater concern was her fear that other students would see she was gaining weight.

As a result of a discussion on goal setting in her personal fitness class, she made up her mind to lose 10 pounds, which would help reduce her percentage of body fat. She also decided she wanted to be able to run the mile at least 2 minutes and 15 seconds faster, which would raise her to the 50th percentile level (10:15) for her age. Jodi wanted to do this in nine weeks, by the time of her next physical fitness test.

After writing down her goals, Jodi made the following list of benefits she would gain from accomplishing her two goals.

a. Her appearance would be improved.

b. She would be less self-conscious with her friends.

c. She would feel good about herself because she had accomplished a difficult task.

d. She would be more physically fit and confident in physical education class.

e. She would be more willing to dress out for physical education.

f. She would be able to wear clothes at least one size smaller.

g. She would feel more confident about tackling other challenges in her life.

GOAL ONE

Jodi knew that in order to successfully reach her two long-term goals, she would have to set several short-term goals. She developed the following plan to meet her goals.

Jodi recognized that her diet contained too much junk food, but she did not know how much. Her first step was to monitor and record everything she ate and drank for three days. This provided her with information about the amount and kinds of foods she was eating. An analysis of her daily food intake revealed that she ate very few fruits and vegetables, frequently went to fast-food restaurants, and ate too much junk food.

Jodi realized that she was eating too much junk food.

Jodi made a decision to eat more appropriately.

Based on her findings and the information obtained on nutrition in Chapter 9, she resolved to:

a. eat at fast-food restaurants no more than twice a week and to make good choices when she did

b. reduce the amount of junk food she was eating and replace it with nutritious snacks

c. eat at least two fruits and three vegetables every day.

Jodi knew these three changes in her nutritional behavior would not be easy to make, but she was tired of being just a "little overweight."

GOAL TWO

In order to reduce her mile-run time by 2 minutes and 15 seconds, Jodi knew she not only had to run more often, but she also had to be more active in general. To meet this long-term goal she resolved to:

a. buy a pair of comfortable jogging shoes that would provide good arch support,

b. walk or jog three times a week at school for 15 minutes without worrying about how far she traveled during the next four weeks

c. cycle or play tennis with one of her parents or a friend at least twice a week

d. jog continuously for 15 minutes by the end of the fifth week,

e. reduce her time for the mile-run at least one minute (11:20) by the end of the fifth week,

f. increase her three training runs at school to 20 minute-durations by the sixth week,

g. retake the test for the mile-run and achieve the 50th percentile level by the end of the ninth week.

Throughout the nine weeks, Jodi planned to weigh herself at the same time each Friday with the anticipation of losing from one to one-and-a-half pounds each week. To help her accomplish her goals, she decided to keep a personal log of her efforts in both areas. She thought that recording her feelings and activities throughout the nine weeks would motivate her to maintain her momentum. She also planned to share her log with her physical education teacher and close friends who she knew would give her feedback and encouragement.

When she reached the end of the nine-week period and achieved both of her goals, she planned to celebrate by buying herself a new outfit. Jodi believed very strongly that she would reach her goals.

Jodi decided to begin jogging & playing tennis.

Jodi is excited about buying some new clothes of a smaller size.

Do you think Jodi was successful in reaching her goals? What were the steps she took? She certainly had all of the elements necessary to be successful since she:

a. had both the desire to improve and a belief that she could do it

b. assessed herself and knew where she was in both of her goal areas

c. identified how she would benefit from reaching her goals

d. set a very specific plan with specific time lines as to when she hoped to accomplish certain things

e. monitored her progress and planned to get the help of her physical education teacher to give her feedback and direction

f. believed in herself and did not give up.

Jodi had concerns similar to those of a lot of young people. She not only wanted to look and feel as good as possible, but she wanted also to perform as well as she could. If you develop a plan tailored to meet your needs, there is no doubt that you will become a successful goal setter.

SUMMARY

The teen years can be a difficult as well as a positive time. Learning to take control of your life through good decision-making can be very rewarding. You will find that effective goal setting will be a natural positive force in your life. If done properly, the process will give you added confidence and a stronger belief in yourself, as you take control of various aspects of your life.

The following are steps in goal setting:

1. Have the desire to improve.
2. Believe that you will be successful.
3. Analyze where you are right now.
4. Set realistic goals.
5. Write down your long- and short-term goals in detail.
6. List benefits you will receive by reaching your goals.
7. Identify the obstacles that may be in your way.
8. Identify the knowledge you may need to reach your goals.
9. Make a plan of action to reach your goals.
10. Develop time lines for both short-term and long-term goals.
11. Monitor your progress closely with a personal log.
12. Never give up.

By keeping your goals appropriate, attainable, and as specific as possible, you will gain momentum to continue on to the next challenge. Remember that goal setting and planning are ongoing processes; therefore, feel free to modify and adapt your plans so that they remain appropriate for you. Do not be upset with yourself if you deviate from your program on a given day. That is human nature. Goal setting may not be easy at first, but it will become easier as you gain experience. Goal setting can become an exciting process in your life. Do not hold back; give it your best shot.

Goal setting is a lot like golf. It's the follow-through that counts.

STUDY QUESTIONS

TRUE-FALSE

The following is a list of some things that you might do as you work toward your goals. Circle "T" if the statement describes what you should do to achieve your goals. Circle "F" if it does not describe what you should do to achieve your goals.

T   F   1.   Avoid setting time lines.

T   F   2.   Use your resources wisely.

T   F   3.   Postpone setting long-term goals.

T   F   4.   List benefits you will receive.

T   F   5.   Ask parents or teachers to set goals for you.

T   F   6.   Write your goals down in detail.

T   F   7.   Do not worry about the obstacles you may face.

T   F   8.   Identify how you will benefit from accomplishing your goals.

T   F   9.   Never readjust your goals.

T   F   10.   Never give up.

DISCUSSION

11.   List two changes that can make your life topsy-turvy.

12.   What goals could you set that might make these changes less stressful?

13.   How are desire and belief in oneself important in accomplishing goals?

14.   What are the steps necessary for successful goal setting?

15.   Identify five goals that you would like to accomplish this year.

GUIDELINES FOR EXERCISE

4

CHAPTER OBJECTIVES

As you read this chapter, look for answers to these key questions:

- What should you consider when beginning an exercise program?

- What clothing considerations should be made for an exercise program?

- What precautions should be taken when exercising in hot weather? In cold weather?

- What are the symptoms of heat exhaustion and heat stroke?

- What other safety factors should you consider when you exercise?

- How do you maintain a proper fluid balance during physical activity?

- What are the steps in warming-up and cooling-down?

- What injuries could you encounter when beginning an exercise program?

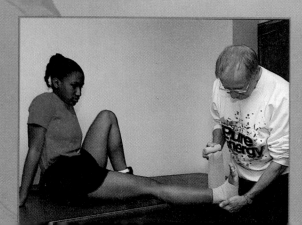

VOCABULARY

When you have completed this chapter, you should understand the meaning of these vocabulary terms:

- hyperthermia
- heat cramps
- heat exhaustion
- heat stroke
- hypothermia
- warm-up
- cool-down
- shin splint
- diaphragm
- stitch in the side

Exercise is to the body as reading is to the mind.

G. LEGMAN

GETTING STARTED

The purpose of this chapter is to help you get a positive start in your personal fitness program. Chapter 14 is specifically designed to help you establish your own personal fitness program. However, it is important that you get started as soon as possible especially if you would like to improve your lifestyle. Chapter 5, Principles of Training, is also related to starting a program since it covers such factors as how hard, how often, and how long you should exercise. There are a number of other important guidelines to keep in mind as you begin your program, they are the focus of this chapter.

MEDICAL EXAM

If you are in good health and have not been ill, you will not need to have a medical exam before beginning a personal fitness program. It is recommended that anyone who has experienced ill health or is over 30 years of age should have a medical exam before beginning a personal fitness program. This is especially important if a person has not been physically active. The medical exam should include what is known as an exercise stress test. During this test, the heart's response to exercise is monitored closely by a physician.

FITNESS EVALUATION

You should evaluate your level of physical fitness prior to beginning a personal fitness program. This will allow you to set realistic goals and to determine your progress over a period of time. Recall that the methods of assessment were discussed in Chapter 2. Assessment should cover all health-related components of physical fitness, including flexibility, cardiovascular fitness, muscular strength and endurance, and body composition.

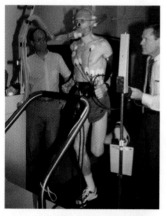

It is important for those over thirty years of age to have a medical exam and an exercise stress test.

Your current level of physical fitness will determine where you should begin exercising and how to progress. Your fitness level data will also help you choose activities that will maintain or improve your current level of physical fitness. Once you have determined your level of fitness, you will be ready to set realistic and challenging goals for your personal fitness program. Your current level of fitness will be the standard by which you will be able to judge your improvement during periodic re-evaluations.

GOAL SETTING

As you know from Chapter 3 goal setting is a key component in establishing a personal fitness program. When setting goals for your personal fitness program, you are really setting lifestyle goals. Your goals should include long- and short-term goals, be realistic, and serve as motivators. Set specific goals that are both attainable and challenging for each health-related component of physical fitness. Evaluate your short-term goals periodically, modifying them as necessary. Your long-term goals may remain the same. Concentrate on improving your lifestyle over a long period of time. Celebrate the fact that you are on a personal trip to becoming a better person.

WHAT YOU WEAR CAN MAKE A DIFFERENCE

Your program and the weather basically determine what you should wear. The general rule is to have good shoes, clean socks that fit, appropriate undergarments, and loose-fitting clothing. Keep in mind that your body's cooling process requires that air pass over the skin to evaporate sweat. Loose clothing allows this evaporative process to take place.

SHOES

Proper footwear is the major requirement for effective care and protection of your feet. Shoes should be designed well, constructed from the best possible materials, and fit well. Purchasing quality athletic shoes is a wise investment. The drawing shows the major features to look for when buying shoes for walking or jogging. When buying athletic shoes, take time to examine them carefully and answer these questions: Do they have good arch supports? Do they have wedge soles at least one-half inch higher at the heel than at the toe? Are the soles at least as wide as the upper part of the shoes? Do they have firm heel cups to hold your feet securely? Do they have soft, well-cushioned inner soles? Are there any rough seams or edges inside the shoes that may cause blisters? Finally, are they the correct size in terms of both width and length? Once you have purchased them, keep your shoes clean and in good repair.

Be a smart consumer when buying shoes. Get advice from a knowledgeable person. Remember, you do not always have to pay a lot of money for quality.

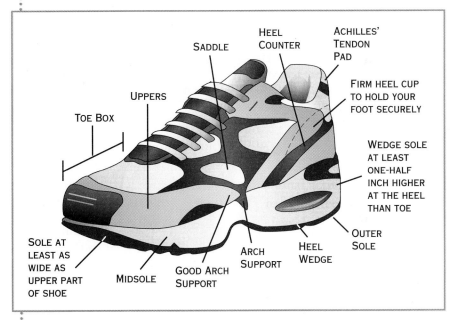

Construction of a Running Shoe

SOCKS

When you try on athletic shoes, be sure to wear the same type of socks you will be wearing when you participate in your fitness activity. A minor factor such as socks may change the fit of the shoes slightly and cause them to feel uncomfortable when you exercise. Socks prevent direct friction of the skin against the shoes, which may cause blisters. In general, it is better to wear two pairs of socks, since this provides more comfort and protection against blisters. Regardless of whether you wear one or two pairs of socks, be sure your socks are clean and fit properly. Make sure there are no wrinkles or folds in your socks before putting on your shoes.

SHIRTS

A regular T-shirt is very appropriate for most activities. Such shirts are predominantly cotton, which provides excellent absorbency and allows the body to breathe. In addition, they are comfortable, durable, easy to wash, and inexpensive. Nylon shirts make cooling more difficult because this material traps sweat, thereby not allowing body heat to be transferred to the air. Common sense tells you never to wear dark-colored shirts at night because of safety considerations and to wear a white shirt in hot weather because white best reflects the sun's rays.

Dress as lightly as possible in hot weather.

SHORTS

The main concern in choosing shorts is that they should not be too tight around the thighs. A tight fit may rub and chafe the body. To reduce irritation and chafing, rub petroleum jelly on your legs where your shorts come in contact with the skin.

EXERCISING IN HOT WEATHER

The maintenance of your body's internal temperature is very important. When you exercise, blood flow is concentrated in the working muscles, creating a heat buildup. This is caused by your blood transferring internal heat from your working muscles to the skin, where it is given off to the outside air. You rely on the air's absorption of heat from your skin surface to keep your body temperature from climbing too high.

A warm environment with high humidity makes the transfer of heat to the air very difficult. Although sweating occurs, the sweat produced fails to evaporate because the air is full of moisture, and there is no place for the liquid sweat to go. This causes less body heat to be transferred to the air. Your body temperature continues to rise and could create a fluid deficiency in your body if you keep exercising.

A reduction of body fluids or an increase in body temperature, called **hyperthermia**, can create conditions that are uncomfortable and even life threatening. It is, therefore, very important for those who exercise in warm or hot environments to learn the symptoms, treatment, and preventive measures for the heat-related body conditions of heat cramps, heat exhaustion, and heat stroke.

Heat cramps are the least serious heat-related problem. Certain muscles (frequently the calf muscle) will contract involuntarily and cause pain. If this happens to you, stop the activity, apply direct pressure, rest, and drink plenty of water.

Exercise with caution in a hot environment.

Heat exhaustion is a condition characterized by profuse sweating accompanied by dizziness and extreme weakness. You should stop physical activity and immediately try to cool the body. Take fluids continuously until the symptoms have passed. Moving to a shaded area and applying wet towels will also help.

Heat stroke is a real medical emergency. This condition is characterized by hot, dry skin and a rising body temperature that may reach 106 degrees. On occasion, unconsciousness may follow. Seek medical assistance immediately. Every attempt must be made to cool the body with an ice massage, cool water immersion, or by any other means.

Heat illness, symptoms, and treatment. The following table presents an outline of heat illnesses. Everyone should be familiar with these conditions and how to protect against them.

	If you have any of the symptoms below, you may be developing a heat injury.		Be prepared to take appropriate actions.	
Heat Cramps	• Thirst • Chills • Clammy skin	• Throbbing heart heat • Nausea	You should: • Drink ½ cup of water every 10–15 minutes	• During breaks, move to shade and remove as much clothing as possible
Heat Exhaustion	• Profuse sweating • Dizziness • Headache • Shortness of breath	• Weak, rapid pulse • Lack of saliva • Extreme fatigue	You should: • Stop exercise and move to a cool environment • Drink 2 cups of water for every pound lost	• Take off wet clothing and sit on a chair in a cold shower • Place an ice bag on your head
Heat Stroke 911	• Lack of sweat • Dry, hot skin • Lack of urine • Hallucinations • Swollen tongue • Deafness	• Visual disturbances • Aggression • Unsteady walking • Excessively high body temperature	You should: • Call for emergency medical treatment • Until help arrives, place ice bags on back and front of head	• Remove clothing and rub alcohol over most of the body • Sit on chair in cold shower

PREVENTIVE MEASURES FOR HEAT ILLNESS

There are several important points to remember when exercising in a hot or humid environment.

1. Light-weight and perforated clothing with adequate exposure of arms and legs promote the escape of heat from the skin surfaces. Lighter colors are preferred since they reflect rather than absorb the sun's rays.

2. Rubberized suits do not promote permanent weight reduction, as many people believe. Such suits can be very dangerous because they cause an elevation of the internal body temperature.

3. Drink fluids before, during, and following your exercise sessions. Do so whether you are thirsty or not. Interestingly enough, when your body is in some stage of dehydration, thirst is not always a good indicator of your body's need for fluids. You should drink two quarts of water each day even if you are not participating in a physical fitness program.

Drink water before, during, and after exercising.

4. Wear a light-weight and light-colored cap to shade your head from the sun.

5. The use of salt tablets is not recommended. Excessive salt tends to irritate the stomach lining and has also been indicated as a risk factor in high blood pressure.

6. On extremely hot and humid days, it is recommended that you confine your exercise to a water environment and/or exercise early or late in the day when the heat is less intense.

If you are exercising with a friend whose skin becomes flushed and hot, whose breathing becomes difficult, or who appears incoherent, get him or her immediate medical help. Follow the above safety guidelines even in cooler weather since the body can also have difficulty cooling itself even when the weather is not hot.

EXERCISING IN COLD WEATHER

Exposure to severe winter like conditions, including below-freezing temperatures, icy winds, and precipitation, can also create serious problems. These conditions can result in an excessive decline in body temperature, or **hypothermia,** as well as cause frostbite, freezing of the limbs and exposed portions of the face. Even if you are fit, be sure to increase your warm-up time and start your exercise slowly with a more gradual energy output than normal. Be aware of the fact that the colder you are, the lower your potential level of operational effectiveness.

Dress in layers and cover your head and hands to prevent heat loss during cold weather.

If you participate in such cold weather activities as jogging, ice skating, skiing, or sled riding, you can offset the effects of your exposure to very cold temperatures and winds by taking the following precautions.

1. Use thermal underwear and outerwear.

2. Wear gloves, face mask, and hat.

3. Wear several layers of light clothing. These are more protective and less cumbersome than one heavy, bulky layer and can be discarded more readily if no longer needed.

4. Do not overdress, since too much clothing can cause you to perspire excessively, making your clothes wet. Damp clothing can be uncomfortable and also cause you to feel chilled.

5. Wear water-resistant outer garments when exposed to snow or a cold rain. Hypothermia tends to occur more rapidly when clothing is wet, even in temperatures above freezing. Wet clothing provides little insulation and actually accelerates the loss of internal body heat.

ADDITIONAL SAFETY PRECAUTIONS

HAVE YOU BEEN UNDER THE WEATHER?

If you are not feeling well, you should stop exercising until you feel better. Whenever there is a chance that physical activity may aggravate a minor illness, infection, or injury, you should quit exercising until you are feeling better. If you are recovering from an illness, begin physical activity at a lower level than that at which you were exercising before your illness.

SHOULD YOU EXERCISE AFTER A BIG MEAL?

The answer to this question centers on the definition of a big meal. If you have just eaten a typical Thanksgiving dinner, you should decrease or suspend vigorous physical activity for two or three hours. However, a leisurely walk with family or friends after the meal will not interfere with digestive processes. School lunches are not considered big meals; therefore, you do not have to worry about how much you eat prior to physical activity. Whenever you are going to participate in a very vigorous sports activity, eat a light meal, so you will be able to perform more efficiently and feel good while you are performing.

It has been found that exercising before a meal will reduce your appetite. If you want to lose weight, participating in your personal fitness program before a meal may be the best time to do so.

If you have been under the weather, start back slowly.

Air pollution

If you live near a big city, you may see people exercising near heavily traveled highways or other areas where there is a high degree of air pollution. If at all possible, find another area, such as a park, in which to exercise. The upper portion of your air passages has an outstanding filtering system for most of the large particles found in air. On the other hand, it has been shown that very small particles are not filtered out of the air and can end up in your lungs. The benefits of exercise tend to outweigh the dangers, but exercising during smog alerts common to some areas should be avoided.

If possible, exercise in less polluted areas.

Dogs

Dogs can pose a problem for walkers, joggers, and cyclists. While their bark is usually more serious than their bite, the exceptions can be very hazardous. Dogs tend to be very protective of their territory, so avoiding them makes sense.

Personal safety

If possible, exercise with another person or with a group. Many people find it easier to stick with an exercise program if they exercise with friends, and also there is safety in numbers. People can sometimes be far more dangerous than dogs. Females, in particular, must be alert to dangerous situations. Exercising with others, staying away from unpopulated areas, eliminating outdoor, nighttime exercise, and staying alert can help avoid danger.

The **warm-up** is a 10- to 15-minute period during which you prepare your body for vigorous exercise. Some people want instant success and forego the warm-up. Such impatience invites pain and injury. A warm-up is very helpful from both a physical and mental standpoint and may determine whether or not you continue to participate in the activity selected.

Start with a brisk walk or slow jog, then stop and do 7–10 minutes of stretching exercises.

BENEFITS OF WARMING UP

It makes sense that warm muscles can be safely stretched more than cold muscles. The more flexible your muscles are, the more you can minimize injuries sustained during a slip or stumble. In addition, a loose and flexible body can better react to and absorb sudden falls and awkward positions that are potential aspects of vigorous exercise. In summary, a warm-up will not bring about early fatigue or hinder performance, but it will prepare the body for activity and help prevent injury. You will find that a warm-up will energize you and make exercising more fun.

Engaging in a proper warm-up period before you exercise:

1. helps you mentally focus your effort and makes you feel like moving.

2. increases your heart rate and the blood supply to your muscles, thus preparing your cardiovascular and muscular systems for the workout.

3. generates heat in the muscle and joint tissues, which makes them more flexible and resistant to injury.

HOW TO WARM-UP

A warm-up usually includes a general and a specific component. The general component has two stages. The first stage includes some type of large muscle activity such as running in place or slow jogging. This activity is designed to raise the heart rate slowly while increasing muscle temperature. The second stage involves static stretching. Muscles should be stretched slowly for 15 to 30 seconds and progressively to the point of discomfort, not pain.

The specific component of a warm-up involves participation in the activity to be performed or a related activity. For example, if you are jogging, you might jog the first half mile of the workout at a leisurely pace, slowly increasing to the desired speed. In this way, your body is allowed to gradually adapt to the specific stress being imposed upon it. Some people use the movements of their sport to warm up. If you are going to play tennis, for example, you will want to warm-up your shoulder and arm muscles. You might want to volley the ball back and forth across the net with your partner or practice a few serves before starting the game.

There is a misconception that warm-ups should be done only when you engage in aerobic activities. Warming up is important in all activities. The concepts of general and specific warm-up apply to biking, jogging, racquetball, rope jumping, swimming, tennis, weight lifting, and all other activities.

The warm-up must become a habit. Many people do not warm up properly but come through without any apparent problems. To be on the safe side, warm up.

COOLING DOWN

The **cool-down** is a 10- to 15-minute period of mild exercise that follows your training session and allows your body and heart rate to return to their resting states slowly. Cooling down from exercise is as important as warming up. Just as your body was allowed to speed up gradually, it must also be allowed to slow down gradually.

BENEFITS OF COOLING DOWN

The explanation for a cool-down period following a rigorous workout is not difficult to understand. Blood returns to the heart through a system of vessels called veins. The muscles squeeze the veins and thus push the blood toward the heart. If you stop exercising suddenly, the return blood flow through the veins is reduced. When this happens, the blood return to the heart will drop quickly and may cause the blood to pool in your legs. This will result in less oxygen going to other body parts, such as the head.

Engaging in a proper cool-down period after you exercise

1. helps to prevent blood from pooling in the muscles you were using. Without a cool-down, less blood reaches your heart, and you may feel light-headed.

2. prevents tightened muscles from becoming sore.

HOW TO COOL-DOWN

Your cool-down should be as long as, or even slightly longer than, your warm-up. The first phase of cooling down should consist of walking or some other light activity to prevent blood from pooling in the muscles you were using. Your cool-down period should continue until your heart rate is around 100 beats per minute.

For your cool-down, repeat some of the same stretching exercises you performed during the warm-up.

The second phase of a cool-down should focus on the same stretching exercises that were used during the warm-up period. You will probably find that stretching is easier after exercising due to the increase in muscle temperature. Stretching at this time loosens tightened muscles and helps prevent muscle soreness.

Bent-leg sit-ups may be added to the cool-down routine. Strong abdominal muscles are a postural aid because they provide support for the upper torso. Many researchers and physical education teachers believe the cool-down is as important or more important than the warm-up.

COMMON INJURIES

If you start your program sensibly and in a gradual manner, the likelihood of incurring any injuries is greatly reduced. However, it is important to be able to recognize the symptoms of some of the more common injuries that people involved in physical activity encounter.

MUSCLE SORENESS

Muscle soreness is a very common problem that usually appears within the first 12 to 24 hours following exertion. In almost all cases, it is the result of starting a program that is too strenuous for you. The discomfort is thought to be due to chemical changes in the muscles and microscopic tears in the muscle fibers and connective tissues. The soreness may be very noticeable and may persist for one to two days. It does diminish gradually. Light massage, easy static stretching, and mild exercise may also be of value in reducing the discomfort. The key point is that nearly all of this pain can be eliminated simply by starting your program in a cautious manner.

BLISTERS

A blister is the result of friction creating heat, tissue damage, and fluid accumulation between the layers of skin in an attempt to prevent further tissue damage. The fluid may be clear or it may be bloody, creating a blood blister.

A blister can be extremely painful. If it breaks, it must be treated as if it were an open wound. After the wound is cleansed, a sterile dressing should be applied. If the blister is unbroken, then two approaches may be considered. First, it may be protected from pressure by applying appropriate gauze padding to it. Another way of protecting the blister is to place a doughnut-shaped piece of foam over it. A second method of treating a blister is to puncture its side with a sterilized needle to release the accumulated fluid. Then it must be treated with an antiseptic and covered tightly. The dressing must be kept clean to reduce the chances of infection. Never remove the layer of skin that covers a blister unless it has been torn loose. This skin covering aids in protecting the sensitive underlying and newly forming layer of skin.

SHIN SPLINTS

A **shin splint** is an overuse syndrome (you did too much too quickly) that will typically develop in poorly conditioned individuals at the beginning of their programs. The pain may be caused by a strain to one or several muscles located in the lower leg or from inflamation of tissue connecting the two bones of the lower leg. Hard surfaces, improper shoes, running on the balls of your feet, and overdoing it in general are the primary reasons for developing shin splints. Treatment consists of rest, ice packs, taping the sore area, and elevation of the leg or legs.

STITCH IN THE SIDE

A **stitch in the side** may develop in individuals who are beginning a jogging program. It is a sharp pain in the side, just under the ribs. While the cause is unknown, there are a number of theories. Some think it is caused by faulty breathing, reduced blood flow to the area, or accumulation of lactic acid in and around the **diaphragm**—a large muscle in your upper abdomen. If you experience this pain, apply pressure to the affected area, stretch to the opposite side and breathe deeply. Once you are in good physical condition, you will rarely experience this type of pain.

Direct pressure to the affected area may give you some relief from a "stitch-in-the-side."

SPRAINED ANKLE

Sprains are injuries to ligaments surrounding a joint or to the capsule-like sac that surrounds a joint. Although a severe sprain may not be distinguishable from a more serious fracture except by X ray, you should stop the activity, apply ice, elevate the injured part, and immobilize the ankle.

SUMMARY

It is very important when beginning a personal fitness program to follow certain guidelines or steps. The first step is to clearly outline what you want to do and then begin in low gear. Many people begin too quickly and become injured. Understanding weather conditions and heat-related illnesses that may occur when exercising outside is of extreme importance. In hot weather, people may exercise too hard and lose too much water from their bodies by sweating. Drinking plenty of water before, during, and after exercise is a step you should always follow. Warming the body up before exercise and cooling it down after exercise are also very important steps for success in your quest for self-improvement.

Success is the name of the game. There is nothing like self-improvement to offset a bored attitude toward your program. Knowing the level you started at and the progress you have made are key factors in success.

The last step is having patience. Seeing real changes in your performance may take a few weeks. If your body is out of shape, remember that it took a long time for it to get that way. It will, therefore, take you more than a few days to get it back into shape. However, as soon as you get started on your program, you can expect to feel good about yourself since you will be following a positive game plan to improve your lifestyle by looking and feeling as good as possible.

TRUE-FALSE

Circle "T" for all correct statements and "F" for all incorrect ones.

T F 1. Selecting proper shoes is the most important consideration when choosing your exercise wardrobe.

T F 2. The color of clothing does not make any difference when you are exercising in hot weather.

T F 3. It is important that you evaluate your level of fitness prior to beginning a personal fitness program.

T F 4. Microscopic tears in muscle fibers and connective tissue are one cause of muscle soreness after you exercise.

T F 5. Dressing in layers during cold weather is an exercise myth.

T F 6. On a day with high humidity, your body is easily cooled by evaporation because you sweat more.

T F 7. It is best to limit fluid intake to people who are sweating profusely because the water may cause stomach cramps.

T F 8. Shin splints are typically caused by overuse of poorly conditioned muscles.

T F 9. A common treatment for blisters is to place a doughnut-shaped piece of foam over the blister.

T F 10. The exact cause of a stitch in the side is not known.

DISCUSSION

11. Your aunt is starting to take an aerobics class at a local health spa and has been advised to wear appropriate shoes. She does not know anything about athletic shoes and asks you about this matter. What would you tell her about selecting the proper shoes?

12. You live in Florida and a cousin from Cleveland comes to visit you in July. Your cousin has not been very active, but he wants to get started on a personal fitness program. He wants to exercise in the afternoon since he does not get up very early in the morning. What are some important guidelines you should give him? What should he wear?

13. Design a general and specific warm-up for an activity in which you engage.

14. What is the purpose of cooling down after exercising?

15. Why do so many people complain about muscle soreness the day after a vigorous physical workout?

PRINCIPLES OF TRAINING

5

CHAPTER OBJECTIVES

As you read this chapter, look for answers to these key questions:

- How does the principle of overload increase your fitness level?

- In what three ways is overload accomplished?

- Why is it important for you to progress at a safe rate in your exercise program?

- What principle would you apply if you wished to improve a specific muscle?

VOCABULARY

When you have completed this chapter, you should understand the meaning of these vocabulary terms:

- principle of overload
- F.I.T.
- frequency
- intensity
- time
- principle of progression
- principle of specificity

You will only get out of training what you put into it.

EFFICIENT AND SAFE TRAINING

In order to look good, feel good, and enjoy a healthy lifestyle, it is essential that you engage in regular physical activity. However, before you enter a training program, review the considerations covered in Chapter 4. You must consider your previous involvement in physical activity, present fitness level, present health, and past medical history.

To operate efficiently and avoid injury, you must follow a carefully planned and deliberate training program. There are three basic training principles to be followed in developing your program: overload, progression, and specificity.

PRINCIPLE OF OVERLOAD

In general terms, the various systems of the body will become stronger and function better if increased demands (overload) are placed upon them. While it is important to overload your body so improvement can occur, the stress should not be so severe that your body is unable to adjust. For example, your body would not be able to adapt to an overload of lifting 300 pounds on your first attempt to increase muscular strength. Not only would you be unsuccessful and not enjoy the exercise session, but you might also cause harm to your body.

As previously mentioned, physical fitness is a personal matter. The amount of overload needed varies with each individual. Some of your friends may have to work more on flexibility, whereas you may have to work harder on muscular endurance. The amount of overload needed by different individuals can easily be seen when comparing a young person and an older person. For example, if your grandmother has been inactive for some time, she may find a fast walk stressful, while you may have to jog for two miles to achieve an overload.

Milo of Crotona—legendary use of overload principle to develop strength

One of the first known examples of the **principle of overload** was traced back to the legendary Milo of Crotona. This famous Greek athlete increased his strength by lifting a small calf several times a week. As the calf grew heavier and heavier, Milo's muscles became stronger, allowing him to lift more and more weight. Milo's use of the overload principle made him the only person in his village to have the strength to lift a full-size bull.

FREQUENCY/INTENSITY/TIME (FIT)

The principle of overload may be accomplished by increasing one of three variables:

Frequency	(how often you exercise)
Intensity	(how hard you exercise)
Time	(how long you exercise)

FIT is the word formed from the first letter of each of the three variables. FIT serves as a reminder of the three ways to achieve overload in your physical fitness program.

FREQUENCY

Frequency refers to the number of times you exercise. Exercise must be performed regularly if you intend to reach and maintain an adequate level of physical fitness. Ideally, your exercise program will become a daily habit, just like brushing your teeth. You can imagine the effects of not brushing your teeth on a regular basis. Similarly, there is a connection between how frequently you exercise and your outward appearance (looking good) and how healthy you are (feeling good). Limiting your exercise to weekend recreational activity is like brushing your teeth only on these days. Exercising three days a week is the minimum frequency (how often you exercise) and will increase your level of fitness if the time (how long you exercise) is increased.

FIT = **F**REQUENCY + **I**NTENSITY + **T**IME

SUN.	MON.	TUES.	WED.	THUR.	FRI.	SAT.
	1	2	3	4	5	6
7	8	9	10	11	12	13
14	15	16	17	18	19	20
21	22	23	24	25	26	27
28	29	30	31			

- AT LEAST 3 TIMES PER WEEK

- 20 MINUTES TO 60 MINUTES DURATION OF TIME RECOMMENDED

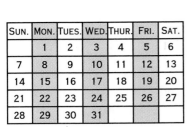

- 60-90% MAXIMAL HEART RATE

How often you exercise depends on your goals. If you want the cardiorespiratory benefits of aerobic exercise, you should exercise at least three times a week. Exercising five times a week, however, is more effective. If you want to lose weight, most experts recommend exercising moderately six days a week. Weight

FIT can be used to remember the methods to increase overload.

training, however, requires time for the muscles to rest and recover. Therefore, a specific muscle should not be overloaded more than every other day for muscular strength or endurance training.

INTENSITY

The **intensity** of all exercise should be increased enough to demand more effort than usual from the body. How hard you must work is a critical question, since very strenuous exercises may cause injury, while not training hard enough will result in little or no improvement. If you have been playing soccer on a regular basis, jogging one mile twice a week will not be enough of a workout to improve your cardiovascular fitness.

How hard should you exercise to develop an acceptable level of fitness? It depends upon the fitness component (cardiovascular, muscular strength and endurance, or flexibility) and your present level of fitness. To improve your cardiovascular fitness, you must make your heart work harder than it normally does. The intensity of a cardiovascular workout is indicated by the number of times per minute your heart beats during the workout—the more intense the exercise the faster your heart rate. Making your heart work harder by running faster would be one application of intensity that would improve cardiovascular fitness. Besides running, swimming, bicycling, and aerobic dance will develop cardiovascular fitness. For muscular strength and endurance you must work harder, or increase intensity, by lifting more weight. To increase intensity for flexibility improvement, you have to work harder by stretching the muscle beyond its normal length.

TIME

Time refers to how long you exercise. How many minutes do you jog (cardiovascular), lift weights (muscular strength and endurance), or perform stretching exercises (flexibility)? In order to be effective, a training session must be maintained for a certain length of time. For example, to develop cardiovascular fitness you need to maintain the activity for at least 20 minutes.

Research shows that as time is increased, intensity is decreased. This means that a beginner can spread the training session over a longer period of time at an easier pace. Rather than biking four miles in 15 minutes, bike the same distance in 20 minutes at an easier pace. People who are excessively overweight should walk instead of jog (lower intensity level) and limit the workout to a 15- or 20-minute session. Gradually they should work up to a longer period of time.

Skipping a workout session to permit the body to rest is acceptable and may help prevent injuries. However, be careful not to let a one-day layoff turn into two days, then three, and so on, until you stop exercising altogether.

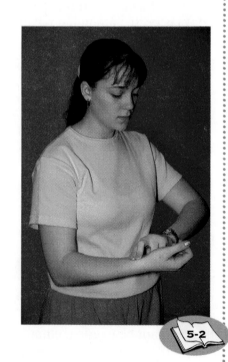

5-2

PRINCIPLE OF PROGRESSION

As you work harder (overload), your body adapts. Because your body becomes accustomed to the workload, you must progressively increase the amount of work for improvement to occur. If you progressively increase the load, as Milo of Crotona did, you will improve fitness and prevent injuries. For example, cardiovascular fitness would be improved if you began a training program that involved running one mile a day in eight minutes for several weeks. However, if you continued to run the same distance in the same amount of time after your body had adapted to this workload, cardiovascular improvement would stop. To continue improving, you would have to increase your intensity by running one mile in seven minutes or increase your distance to one and a half miles. This would again put the overload principle into effect. Over a period of time, additional overload would have to be added.

It is very important that you know when it is safe to progress. Think of the **principle of progression** as the schedule for the application of overload. You want to slowly and progressively apply stress to the body only when it is needed and not before. This is especially true during the first four to six weeks of your program, in which you should increase the overload very slowly. If your exercise level is too intense or your exercise session too long, you may feel unusually tired during the session or even for a few hours after it. This is a signal that you have placed too much overload on your body. Other signs of overexertion include nausea or vomiting during or after a workout and muscle or joint aches and pains that do not go away quickly. If you experience any of these

TRAIN - DON'T STRAIN

Gradually increase overload.

symptoms, you need to reduce your exercise intensity and time. This is why it is important to evaluate the health-related components of physical fitness and to record daily achievements. With records of progress and knowledge of training principles, you will know when it is safe to progress and increase your overload.

PRINCIPLE OF SPECIFICITY

The **principle of specificity** refers to the specific exercises that improve specific components of physical fitness in specific body parts. For example, flexibility exercises will increase flexibility but will not necessarily improve cardiovascular fitness. Stretching your legs will not increase flexibility in your arms. Another example is when a person who has trained for a specific sport such as gymnastics, attempts to play basketball and quickly becomes fatigued. Each physical activity requires specific demands, and doing the activity is the best way to train for it.

You must do specific exercises to improve cardiovascular fitness.

SUMMARY

Three basic training principles (overload, progression, and specificity) must be observed when you design an exercise program. An overload must be added beyond what is normally placed on the body in daily activity. You can place overload on the body by increasing one or more of the overload variables: **frequency** (how often you work), **intensity** (how hard you work), and **time** (how long you work). A good way to remember the three overload variables is to think of the word FIT—Frequency, Intensity, Time.

Body systems adapt to the specific stresses placed upon them. As your body adapts to stress, you must progressively increase the overload to improve your level of fitness. The principle of progression allows you to increase overload gradually without injury or discomfort.

The principle of specificity permits you to improve a specific component of physical fitness in specific body parts. To improve a specific component, you must select the appropriate physical activity. The overload for a given exercise will vary for each individual. Remember that injuries result when progression is not gradual and overload is added too quickly.

STUDY QUESTIONS

TRUE-FALSE

Circle "T" for all correct statements and "F" for all incorrect ones.

T F 1. When starting a physical fitness program, you do not need to consider your present fitness level.

T F 2. To avoid injury, you should gradually increase the intensity of your workout.

T F 3. If you increase the length of time of your exercise session, you are likely to decrease the level of intensity.

T F 4. Teenagers who are overweight may need to decrease the intensity of their workouts as well as the length of time of their exercise sessions.

T F 5. Applying the principle of specificity means that you can increase leg strength by doing pull-ups.

MULTIPLE CHOICE

Place the letter of the best answer in the space provided.

.... 6. Progression means
A. slowly increasing the amount of exercise.
B. changing from running to tennis.
C. starting easy and going for a long period of time.
D. starting fast to improve quickly.

.... 7. The legendary Milo of Crotona became stronger by applying the principle of
A. specificity.
B. all or none.
C. regression.
D. overload.

.... 8. When you increase the workload of your training session, you are increasing
A. frequency.
B. intensity.
C. time.
D. specificity.

.... 9. When you increase the length of your workout, you are increasing
A. frequency.
B. intensity.
C. time.
D. specificity.

.... 10. Frequency refers to how
A. hard you exercise.
B. often you exercise.
C. long you exercise.
D. fast you exercise.

DISCUSSION

11. Why must an overload be placed on the body to improve physical fitness?

12. Why does the amount of overload vary from individual to individual?

13. How did Milo of Crotona progressively increase his workload?

14. Why must you progressively increase the amount of work in order for improvement to occur?

15. Give an example of an exercise or activity you engage in and state how the principle of specificity is involved.

FLEXIBILITY

6

CHAPTER OBJECTIVES

As you read this chapter, look for answers to these key questions:

- How is joint movement limited?
- Why is flexibility important?
- What is the difference between static stretching and dynamic stretching?
- How may the training principles be applied to improve flexibility?
- What safety precautions should be taken when you are engaging in flexibility exercises?
- How is flexibility evaluated?

VOCABULARY

When you have completed this chapter, you should understand the meaning of these vocabulary terms:

- joint
- ligament
- muscle
- tendon
- static stretching
- dynamic stretching
- ballistic stretching
- isostatic stretching

6-1

The rubber band theory applies to each of us; we will be no good until stretched.

WHAT IS FLEXIBILITY?

What comes to your mind when the word flexibility is mentioned? Do you think of a circus acrobat tumbling about, a yoga instructor with legs behind his head, or a dancer doing splits? Everyone has flexibility to some degree, even the armchair athlete.

Flexibility is the ability to move body joints through a full range of motion. A **joint** is the point at which two bones come together. Examples of joints are the wrists, elbows, shoulders, hips, knees, and ankles. Notice that all joints do not move in the same way or to the same degree. The amount of movement in a joint is limited by the way it is formed. Pivot joints, such as the neck, permit a rotating motion. Hinge joints, such as the knee, permit a back and forth motion, while the hip and shoulders have a ball-and-socket formation, allowing for movement in many different directions. Your wrists and ankles have gliding joints that allow bones to slide over one another.

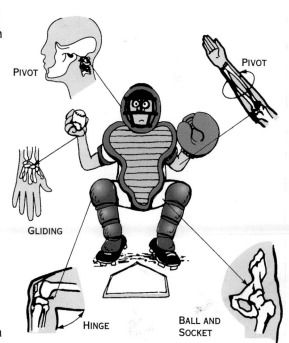

Joints of the human body

HOW IS JOINT MOVEMENT LIMITED?

The direction in which a joint moves cannot be changed because of bone structure. For example, the bone structures of the elbow and knee joints set a very definite limit on how far the arm and leg can extend. These are mechanical factors that cannot be greatly modified. In other joints, such as the ankle and hip, the limitation on range of motion is imposed by soft tissue and can be modified. This soft tissue is in the form of **ligaments**, **muscles**, and **tendons**. It is possible to improve the amount of motion in a joint by performing exercises that alter these soft tissues.

Ligament:	strong fibrous tissue that attaches one bone to another
Muscle:	meaty tissue that surrounds bones
Tendon:	connective tissue that anchors the muscle to bone

To help you remember what makes up soft tissue, think of the terms in alphabetical order. First, ligaments attach bone to bone. Then, muscles cover over or surround the bone. Finally, tendons anchor the muscle to the bone.

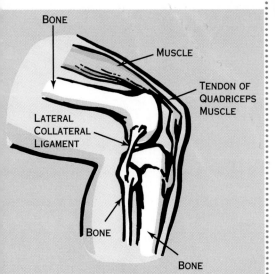

BONE

MUSCLE

TENDON OF QUADRICEPS MUSCLE

LATERAL COLLATERAL LIGAMENT

BONE

BONE

Soft tissue limits flexibility.

WHY IS FLEXIBILITY IMPORTANT?

A reasonable amount of flexibility (joint movement) is required to live a healthy and functional life both at work and play. Since the loss of flexibility occurs gradually, you probably will not realize you are experiencing a decrease in flexibility until a problem arises. Almost everyone has observed older adults and noticed that some are more flexible than others. This is due in part to the amount of activity in which they are presently engaged and past activity in which they were engaged.

Individuals of the same age may have different levels of flexibility due to past and present physical activity.

REDUCES INJURIES

A lack of flexibility can result in joint or muscle injury during exercise or daily activities. While your strength and aerobic capacity will increase with exercise, your flexibility, in some cases, may decrease with weight training and aerobic conditioning. For this reason, every muscle strengthened must also be stretched to maintain and improve flexibility as much as possible. All athletes, including professional football players, now supplement their weight training and conditioning programs with stretching exercises that improve flexibility and help reduce the number of injuries.

PREVENTS POST EXERCISE PAIN

Post exercise pain and stiffness caused by muscle spasms can be prevented or reduced by stretching exercises. Including warm-up and cool-down sessions in your workout will stretch shortened muscles and, therefore, help prevent muscular soreness. The warm-up increases the blood supply to your muscles, raises their temperature, and makes them more flexible and resistant to injury. After exercising, a cool-down period of mild exercise can prevent muscle problems by gradually stretching the muscles you used. It can also prevent blood from pooling in the area exercised.

REDUCES CHANCE OF LOW BACK PAIN

Low back pain is one of the most common ailments. It has been estimated that 80 percent of the population in the United States suffers from backaches. Adequate flexibility in the lower back and posterior thighs can do much to reduce these aches and prevent low back problems in adulthood.

HELPS RELIEVE EMOTIONAL TENSION

Tight muscles arise from many causes including emotional tension. Stretching is an exercise that can help relax tense muscles. Stretching the muscles in your neck, shoulders, and upper back is an especially useful way to relax because these muscles often become tense when you sit for long periods. Have you ever seen adults who work in an office stretch or bend their heads from side to side? Have you ever stretched your wrist and arm when taking a written exam? These movements are attempts to relieve tight muscles caused by tension.

TYPES OF STRETCHING

Two types of stretching can safely improve flexibility: static and dynamic. **Static stretching** is the more acceptable method of increasing flexibility. The process involves slowly moving the

Hold stretch for a minimum of fifteen seconds.

muscle to its stretching point and holding this position for 15 to 30 seconds. **Dynamic stretching** involves a similar position but is done in a continuous slow and controlled manner. This method of stretching should not be confused with ballistic or bouncing type stretching in which the motion is done very rapidly. **Ballistic stretching** usually involves bobbing, bouncing, or jerky movements that use the body's momentum. This type of stretching is sometimes harmful because you may exceed the stretchable limits of the tissues involved.

One other type of stretching is called **isostatic stretching**. The initial phase of this type of stretching is static. You extend the stretch to the maximum limit and hold. After eight seconds, a partner pushes you beyond the initial limit as you relax. This form of stretching is not recommended because the partner cannot know how much pain you are experiencing and may force a body part too far, causing injury.

APPLICATION OF TRAINING PRINCIPLES

Stretching for relaxation can be performed anywhere at any time. However, to increase flexibility, you must engage in a more deliberate training program. This could be in the form of a separate flexibility program, or it could be combined with the warm-up and cool-down phases of your overall personal fitness program.

It is very important to raise the muscle temperature prior to developmental stretching. This may be done by brisk walking, jogging, or other mild exercise. Increase muscle temperature before attempting any stretching exercises; otherwise, the flexibility exercises designed to prevent muscular problems may themselves cause problems.

PRINCIPLE OF OVERLOAD

To improve flexibility, you must stretch the soft tissue (ligaments, muscles, and tendons) farther than you are accustomed to doing. This additional overload can be placed on the body by an increase in frequency, intensity, or time of the exercise program.

FREQUENCY—Stretching exercises should be done a minimum of three times per week. Performing them daily is best.

INTENSITY—The muscle is stretched beyond its normal length to reach what is called the stretching point. To reach the stretching point, you stretch slowly until mild tension is felt.

TIME—The length of time a static stretching position is held may be increased gradually from 15 to 30 seconds. Another way to increase time would be to increase the number of repetitions of an exercise, regardless of whether it is a static or dynamic stretch.

Summary of Flexibility Training Guidelines	
Frequency	At least 3 times per week.
Intensity	Stretch slowly until mild tension is felt.
Time	Static: Hold each stretch 15 to 30 seconds.
	Dynamic: Do 10 to 20 repetitions and 1 to 3 sets.

PRINCIPLE OF PROGRESSION

You may gradually increase the overload by increasing (1) the number of sessions per day or week (frequency), (2) the distance the muscle is stretched (intensity), or (3) the amount of time the position is held or the number of repetitions and sets (time). Regardless of how you progressively increase the overload, remember to do so in a slow, easy manner.

PRINCIPLE OF SPECIFICITY

Stretching exercises will improve flexibility only in the joints you exercise. You may be flexible in one joint, but this does not mean you have the same degree of flexibility in all joints. Some of your joints may be unusually flexible, while others may be only somewhat inflexible. Flexibility is also specific to each individual. Females tend to be more flexible than males of the same age. Because flexibility differs with each person, you should not compete with others in how far they stretch. Some sports require flexibility in specific joints not required in other sports. Even within the same sport, flexibility requirements vary widely. For example, a quarterback needs shoulder–joint flexibility in order to throw a perfect pass, while a punter requires greater hip–joint flexibility.

FLEXIBILITY SAFETY PRECAUTIONS

The following safety precautions should be considered when performing flexibility exercises.

1. All ballistic stretching exercises that use the body's momentum to force a muscle beyond its stretching point have the potential for causing injury and should be avoided.

2. Using partners to help you get extra stretch can cause injury because others cannot know how much pain you are in and may force your body too far.

3. Start at a proper level and know when to increase the frequency, intensity, or amount of time of flexibility exercises.

4. There is danger of injury if you attempt to imitate the stretching ability of others. Stretch according to what you feel, not according to what others do.

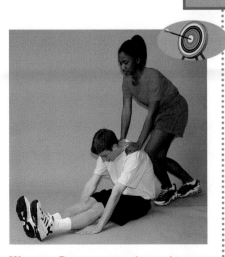

Warning: Partner-assisted stretching can cause injury.

5. Include flexibility exercises with cardiovascular and muscular strength and endurance programs to prevent a muscle imbalance, such as the tight hamstring muscles frequently experienced by joggers.

FLEXIBILILTY ASSESSMENT

You should know your present level of flexibility before beginning an exercise program. Testing the flexibility of each joint would take too much time and require elaborate equipment. The flexibility tests described in the *Personal Fitness: Looking Good/Feeling Good Student Activity Handbook* will give you an indication of flexibility in joints most likely to need attention. A word of caution before you begin testing (1) always warm up properly, (2) avoid ballistic (bouncing-type) movements when performing the tests, and (3) move into the testing position in a slow, controlled manner.

SETTING GOALS TO IMPROVE FLEXIBILITY

Flexibility can be improved rapidly if a person appropriately applies the training principles and the variables of overload. If your flexibility test score is more then 10 cm below the health fitness standard, you should set six-month improvement goals within a range of 5 to 15 cm. If you are close to the standard, set goals with a range of 1 to 4 cm of improvement. If you exceed the health fitness standard, set your goal at 0 to 2 cm.

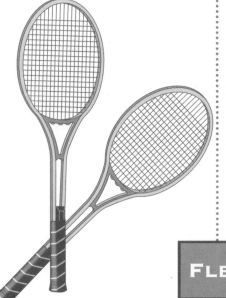

Flexibility Goal Setting			
	Distance from Health Fitness Standard		
	Less	Close	Exceeds
Difference Between Test Score and Health Fitness Standard	more than 10 cm	1 to 10 cm	at or above standard
Recommended Range for Goals	5 to 15 cm	1 to 4 cm	0 to 2 cm

FLEXIBILITY EXERCISES

Even if you score high on the flexibility tests, you should stretch your shoulders, lower back, hips, chest, backs of thighs, and calves on a regular basis. You will need to select specific stretching exercises before engaging in an exercise session or sports activity. The

Upper body and torso stretch

following exercises stretch each of the different parts of the body and will serve as a starting point.

UPPER BODY AND TORSO STRETCH

- Bend the knees of both legs slightly.
- Tuck the buttocks under to keep the spine in a straight line.
- Slowly extend one arm overhead as high as possible while extending the other arm downward.
- Keep the head straight; do not allow it to tilt back.
- Hold the stretch for 15 seconds.
- Repeat with the other arm.

NECK STRETCH

- Slowly bend your neck to the right and then to the left.
- Slowly turn your head to each side.
- Lower your chin to your chest.
- Rotate your head first to the right and then to the left.
- Hold each position for 15 seconds.
- Never bend your neck to the back (hyperextend).
- Emphasis should be on stretching in the various positions and not on rotation.

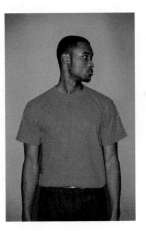
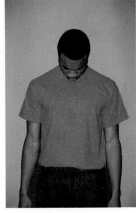

Neck stretch

Triceps stretch

TRICEPS STRETCH

- Reach over your head toward your back with one hand.
- Place the opposite hand on the elbow and apply pressure to the elbow.
- Hold for 15 seconds.
- Repeat with the other arm.

CHEST AND BICEPS STRETCH

- Grasp your hands behind your back.
- Slowly pull your arms toward one another.
- Hold for 15 seconds.

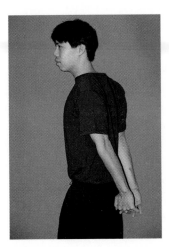

Chest and biceps stretch

Shoulder stretch

SHOULDER STRETCH

- Reach across your chest with one arm.
- Slowly push this arm with your other hand.
- Hold for 15 seconds.
- Repeat with the other arm.

THREE-PRONG SUPPORT SIDE STRETCH

- Kneel on one knee.
- Bend to the same side as the bent knee, and support part of your weight on one arm.
- Extend the other leg out to the side.
- Slowly extend the opposite arm over your head.
- Stretch from the extended leg to the extended arm.
- Hold for 15 seconds.
- Repeat to the other side.

Lower back stretch

Three-prong support side stretch

LOWER BACK STRETCH

- Lie on your back.
- Grasp your legs underneath your knee caps.
- Pull knees to your chest.
- Hold for 15 seconds.

HAMSTRING STRETCH

- Place one foot on a low step or bench.
- Keep the knee bent, and bend from the hips.
- Hold for 15 seconds.
- Repeat with the other leg.

Hamstring stretch

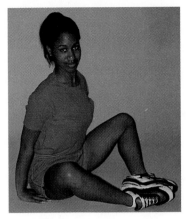
Groin stretch

Quadriceps stretch

GROIN STRETCH

- Sit on the floor, and place the soles of your feet together.
- Pull your feet a comfortable distance into your groin.
- Place hands on the floor to your side to support the back.
- Slowly press the knees down.
- When you feel tension, hold for 15 seconds.

QUADRICEPS STRETCH

- Place left hand on your partner's shoulder or on an object for balance.
- Flex your right leg backwards.
- Grasp your right ankle with your right hand.
- Press the foot into your hand.
- Do not pull on the foot or touch the heel to your buttocks because this will cause a strain on the knee ligament.
- When you feel the stretch in the front of the leg, hold for 15 seconds.
- Repeat for the left leg.

CALF STRETCH

- Stand slightly more than an arm's length from a wall.
- Place your feet a shoulder width apart, flat on the floor.
- Hands should be flat, with knees and body straight.
- Lean forward by bending the elbows.
- When you feel tension in the lower calves, hold for 15 seconds.

ACHILLES TENDON STRETCH

- Stand 2 to 3 feet from a support.
- Place one foot behind the other.
- Lean forward keeping the heels flat.
- Slowly bend the knee of the rear leg until the Achilles tendon is stretched.
- Hold for 15 seconds.
- Repeat with the other foot.

Calf stretch

Achilles tendon stretch

Shin stretch

SHIN STRETCH

- Stand 2 feet from a support.
- Place one foot behind the other.
- Bend the knee of the rear leg with toes to the ground, as shown in the photo.
- Slowly bend until you feel a stretch in the front of the lower leg.
- Hold for 15 seconds.
- Repeat with the other leg.

HARMFUL STRETCHING POSITIONS

- The following stretching positions can be harmful. Many of them put stress on your joints, ligaments, tendons, and muscles and may lead to injury. If you choose to perform any of the exercises listed, remember to stretch in a safe and controlled manner. Always avoid rapid, jerky, bouncy, ballistic movements because they may cause injury.

HEAD CIRCLES

- Never hyperextend your neck or do full head circles.

ARM CIRCLES

- Arm circles are actually ballistic stretches of the shoulder joint.

PLOW

- The plow position compresses the cervical vertebrae of the back and puts a large amount of stress on the lower back.

SITTING QUADRICEPS STRETCH

- Sitting on your heels to stretch the quadriceps overbends the knee joint.

Head Circles

Arm circles

Plow

Sitting quadriceps stretch

FOUR-COUNT TOE TOUCH

- The four-count toe touch is a traditional exercise that has been done for years, so it may be difficult to resist doing it. Just remember that there are alternatives that do not place undue pressure on the disks of the lower spine such as the hamstring stretch. Also, some people tend to lock their knees as they reach downward doing the toe touch. This can hyperextend the knee joint and cause an injury.

Four-count toe touch

HURDLE STRETCH

- The hurdle stretch forces sideway movement of a hinge joint (bent knee joint) that is designed only for flexion and extension.

DEEP KNEE BENDS

- Bending at the knees is essential for safe lifting techniques. However, while keeping the heels flat on the ground, your knees should not bend beyond the point at which your thighs are parallel to the floor. Going beyond this limit may cause injury to any of the structures around the knee, including cartilage.

Hurdle stretch

Deep knee bends

SUMMARY

Flexibility is the ability to move body joints through a full range of motion. The direction of joint movement is limited by the way it is structured. Some joints have a very limited range of motion, while others allow for movement in all directions. The four types of joints are the pivot, hinge, ball-and-socket, and gliding joint. Flexibility improvement can be made by performing static stretching if the limitation on range of motion is imposed by soft tissues (ligaments, muscles, and tendons).

Everyone needs flexibility to some degree both at work and play. An adequate degree of flexibility can reduce injuries, prevent postexercise pain, reduce chance of low back pain, and help in relieving emotional tension.

Static and dynamic stretching can be used to improve flexibility. These stretches can be done as part of the warm-up and cooldown phases of your overall personal fitness program or as a separate flexibility program.

All principles of training are important in the development of flexibility. You should assess your present level of flexibility before beginning the flexibility phase of your personal fitness program.

Ballistic stretching and exercises that hyperextend the neck should not be performed. In addition, activities that compress the vertebrae, overbend a joint, or force sideward movements should be avoided.

STUDY QUESTIONS

TRUE-FALSE

Circle "T" for all correct statements and "F" for all incorrect ones.

T   F   1.   Individuals with good flexibility are less likely to be injured.

T   F   2.   You should bounce as hard as you can when doing flexibility exercises.

T   F   3.   Ligaments help hold joints together.

T   F   4.   Tendons attach muscles to bones.

T   F   5.   Poor muscle development, poor flexibility, or poor posture are factors contributing to the fact that 80 percent of people in the United States suffer from low back pain.

MULTIPLE CHOICE

Place the letter of the correct answer in the space provided.

....   6. Stretching exercises will help
     A. avoid injuries.
     B. build strength.
     C. develop cardiovascular endurance.
     D. none of the above.

....   7. Joints can be prepared for vigorous physical activity by doing
     A. push-ups.   C. stretching.
     B. sit-ups.   D. weight training

....   8. Muscles and other connective tissues should be stretched
     A. three times per week.   C. once a week.
     B. only before jogging.   D. when it is cold.

....   9. To increase flexibility, you must overload the muscle by
     A. increasing your running distance.
     B. lifting heavy weights.
     C. performing isometric exercises.
     D. stretching farther than normal.

....   10. Which exercise below is a safe exercise for developing flexibility?
     A. Achilles tendon stretch
     B. deep knee bends
     C. four-count toe touch
     D. hurdle stretch

DISCUSSION

11.   Why does a person lose flexibility?

12.   What is the major difference between static and dynamic stretching?

13.   How can the overload principle be used to improve flexibility?

14.   Why should you not use partners when performing stretching exercises?

15.   Name a sport or recreational activity in which you participate. List three stretching exercises you could perform to warm up for this activity.

CARDIOVASCULAR FITNESS

7

As you read this chapter, look for answers to these key questions:

- How can you measure your pulse rate?

- What benefits are gained from participation in activities promoting cardiovascular fitness?

- Which health risk factors can be controlled with cardiovascular training?

- How can the training principles be applied to improve cardiovascular fitness?

- How do you determine the rate at which your heart should be exercised?

- How do you know when it is safe to progress with your cardiovascular training?

VOCABULARY

When you have completed this chapter, you should understand the meaning of these vocabulary terms:

- pulse
- resting heart rate
- recovery heart rate
- blood pressure
- atherosclerosis
- maximum heart rate
- target heart rate
- aerobic
- anaerobic

WHY IS CARDIOVASCULAR FITNESS IMPORTANT?

Cardiovascular fitness is said to be the most important of all physical fitness components. No matter how strong you look, if your circulatory and respiratory systems cannot meet your muscles' demand for oxygen, you cannot continue activity for a long period of time.

Exercising to improve cardiovascular fitness will increase your energy level, making it possible for you to exercise longer without tiring, and making you feel good. Additionally, exercising for cardiovascular fitness will help you look good because the exercises will help you control your weight, improve your appearance, and improve your ability to deal with the problems you face daily. You may be one of many people who have a low level of cardiovascular fitness if you find you are short of breath, tire easily, are unable to swim, run, bike or perform physical activities.

> **The race is not always to the swift but to those who keep on trying.**

Developing cardiovascular fitness will help you enjoy life to its fullest.

87

If you are short of breath and left behind, you need to improve your cardiovascular fitness.

Cardiovascular fitness is the body's ability to provide oxygen continuously to muscles as work is performed over an extended period of time. This component of fitness includes the circulatory system (heart, blood, and blood vessels) and the respiratory system (lungs and air passages).

Research has shown that body functions improve with use and decline with disuse. In other words, the heart, lungs, and muscles become stronger and more efficient in their utilization of oxygen when they are used more. To understand how to improve your cardiovascular fitness, you must first understand how the circulatory and respiratory systems function and which diseases may result if these systems are neglected.

CIRCULATORY AND RESPIRATORY SYSTEMS

People often take oxygen for granted and do not think of it as fuel for the body. The fact is, the more oxygen that muscles receive, the more energy they can produce and the better you feel. The circulatory and respiratory systems work together to provide muscles with necessary oxygen. As air is breathed in, the blood picks up oxygen from the lungs and carries it to the heart.

The heart is a remarkable muscle that serves as two pumps. The ventricle on the left side of the heart forces blood containing oxygen throughout the body through elastic blood vessels called arteries. Arteries always carry blood away from the heart.

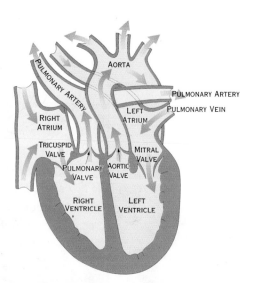

Cross section of the heart. Note the left ventricle muscle walls are thicker than the right ventricle walls, since this chamber pumps blood throughout the body compared to the right ventricle, which only has to pump it to the nearby lungs.

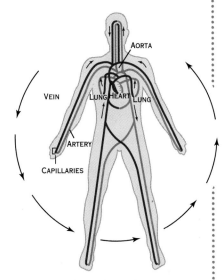

Simplified map of circulatory system. Arrows indicate blood flow out of the heart through arteries and back by way of veins.

As arteries branch out in the body, they gradually decrease in size until they form tiny capillaries. This is where food and oxygen are delivered from the blood to cells throughout the body. In the drawing below notice how the capillaries serve as bridges between arteries and veins. Veins always carry blood toward the heart.

Just as ashes are left after a fire, waste materials remain when cells use up oxygen. These wastes are picked up by the blood in the capillaries and are transported back to the heart by veins. Blood is forced through the veins by contracting muscles. The blood in veins can only move toward the heart, because one-way valves keep the blood from flowing backward when the muscle relaxes. The right ventricle of the heart pumps the returning blood to the lungs, where wastes are exchanged for more oxygen, and the process repeats itself.

Your body holds only about 12 pints of blood. Therefore, the blood must circulate throughout the body to supply all the body cells continuously with oxygen and nutrients and to remove wastes. That is why the heart, blood vessels, and blood are called the circulatory system.

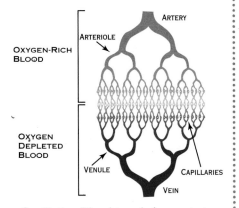

Capillaries. Blood travels from arteries and arterioles into capillaries and then into venules and veins.

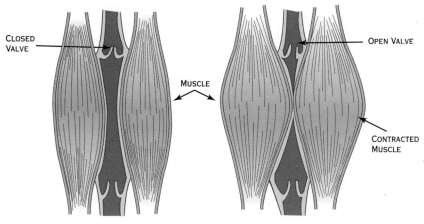

Contracting muscles squeeze the blood through one-way valves toward the heart.

MONITORING THE HEART

How fast must the heart beat to pump blood? Your heart rate varies with the changing needs of your body. When you are lying down, your heart rate is less than when you are standing. Running produces a higher heart rate than doing a less vigorous activity, such as walking. Your size also has an effect on your heart rate. The average heart rate for adults is 70 beats per minute. In children, the heart beats about 100 times per minute. It is important for you to know how hard your heart muscle is working. One way of knowing is to measure your pulse rate.

PULSE

Your **pulse** is caused by pressure of the blood on the artery wall, and it corresponds to your heart beat. The best locations for measuring your pulse rate are at the wrist and neck, where arteries lie just below the skin. To take your pulse at the wrist, place your index and middle finger against the skin at the base of your thumb on the soft area of the wrist.

Pulse may be taken at the wrist or carotid artery. Take the pulse for ten seconds and multiply by six for a one-minute heart rate count.

To measure your pulse rate at the carotid artery of the neck, place your index and middle fingers on the midway point between your ear lobe and your Adam's apple. Once your hand is in the correct position count the number of beats for six seconds and place a zero at the end of that number, or count the beats for ten seconds and multiply by six to obtain a one-minute pulse rate.

Several factors may cause the pulse rate to vary. For example, exercise increases the pulse. The higher the intensity of exercise, the higher the pulse rate. Other factors that may affect the pulse rate include excitement, position of the body, and illness. Since your pulse rate varies throughout the day, it is recommended that you take your pulse at rest if you wish to compare pulse rate readings while exercising.

RESTING HEART RATE

Since the heart is a muscle, it becomes stronger when exercised. By keeping a record of your resting heart rate, you can measure the progress gained in your cardiovascular fitness program. An active person has a lower resting heart rate than someone who is inactive. The heart of an active person pumps more blood with each beat, thus working more efficiently. After a few months of cardiovascular training, a sedentary person will note a decrease in the resting heart rate of ten to 25 beats per minute. This illustrates that your heart is becoming stronger and more efficient.

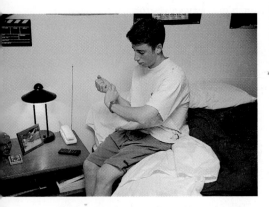

Resting heart rate should be taken first thing in the morning and in the same position.

To measure the **resting heart rate**, take your pulse just after waking in the morning and before getting out of bed. Your pulse should be taken while you are in a sitting or lying position. A range from 50 to 100 beats per minute for a resting heart rate has been established as normal by the American Heart Association. However, research shows that adults with resting heart rates over 70 have a greater risk of heart attack than those with resting heart rates below 70.

RECOVERY HEART RATE

To determine when it is safe to progress in your training program, you should check your pulse after the exercise session to determine your **recovery heart rate**. The guiding principle is that your heart rate should drop to about 120 beats per minute (bpm) within five minutes after the workout and be less than 100 beats per minute after ten minutes.

Monitor recovery heart rate to determine when to progress in your training program.

> ### NORMAL RECOVERY HEART RATE RANGE
>
> 5 minutes after exercise = 120 bpm
> 10 minutes after exercise = 100 bpm

If after five minutes your pulse does not drop to 120 beats per minute, or after ten minutes to 100 beats per minute, you need to reduce the intensity of your workout. On the other hand, you may elect to increase the intensity of your workout if your recovery heart rate is below 120 beats per minute five minutes after exercising and below 100 beats per minute ten minutes after exercising.

BLOOD PRESSURE

Blood pressure is the measure of blood force against the walls of the arteries. Blood pressure is recorded with two numbers. The higher number recorded is the systolic pressure and represents your blood pressure at the moment blood is pumped from the heart by the ventricles. The lower number is the diastolic pressure and represents the blood pressure when the heart is relaxed and filling with blood. The normal range for blood pressure is shown below.

Blood pressure is one external method of monitoring your circulatory system. A high reading indicates an inefficient system.

> ### NORMAL BLOOD PRESSURE RANGE
>
> 120 + or −   systolic pressure
> 80 + or −   diastolic pressure

Aerobic exercises contribute to blood pressure control. Both systolic and diastolic pressures can be reduced as a result of aerobic training. Long-term research studies have shown that the lower the blood pressure, within normal limits (100/70), the lower the risk of having a heart attack.

CARDIOVASCULAR DISEASE

When people are young, they have a tendency to feel indestructible. Many teenagers believe they will live forever and give little thought to illnesses, much less death. What is needed is a mature evaluation of your lifestyle and how it will affect your health in 20 or 30 years. Scientists have found that many illnesses affecting older people start very early in life.

One illness that starts at an early age is cardiovascular disease, which causes 43 percent of deaths in the United States. In fact, it is the major cause of death in our nation. To put it another way, for every American who dies of cancer (the second ranking cause of death) two die of a heart-related illness.

CAUSES OF CARDIOVASCULAR DISEASE

The primary cause of cardiovascular disease is a buildup of fatty deposits on the inner walls of the arteries. These deposits cause arterial passageways to become smaller, leading to a condition called **atherosclerosis**. This restricts the blood flow, much like placing your thumb over a garden hose restricts the flow of water. Just as your thumb causes a higher water pressure in the hose, the fatty deposits on the inner walls of the arteries cause a higher blood pressure, which makes the heart work harder.

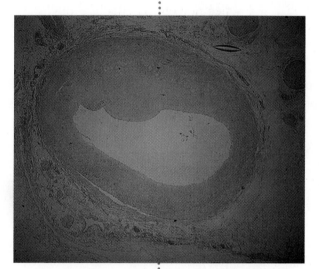 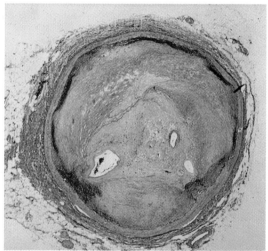

Developing stages of atherosclerosis

These fatty deposits can become so great that blood will not flow through the artery. In addition, blood vessels can also be blocked by a blood clot (thrombosis) lodged in a narrowed passageway. When this happens to an artery that feeds the heart (coronary artery), a heart attack occurs. When it happens to an artery that supplies blood to the brain, a stroke occurs. While either a heart attack or stroke happens suddenly, the factors casuing the blocked arteries can be traced back to a condition that started many years earlier.

RISK FACTORS

 A study of medical records indicates that ailments of the heart and blood vessels have decreased in recent years. However, cardiovascular disease continues to hold the deadly distinction of being the number one killer in the United States. In fact, heart and blood ves-

sel diseases cause almost as many deaths as cancer, accidents, pneumonia, influenza, and all other causes of death. As you will recall from Chapter 1, the risk factors associated with heart attacks are:

1. inactivity
2. obesity
3. high blood pressure
4. high levels of cholesterol
5. stress and tension
6. smoking
7. sex of individual
8. heredity
9. age

As you review the nine risk factors, notice that the first six are controllable. The choices you make today in your lifestyle will have an effect on how well and how long you live when you are older. In fact, many people your parents' age and older wish they had learned the values of exercise and other good health habits when they were much younger.

CARDIOVASCULAR BENEFITS OF EXERCISE

Participating in activities that promote cardiovascular fitness strengthens the heart and reduces atherosclerosis. Active people are better able to clear fats from their blood stream as a result of exercise. Therefore, fatty substances are less likely to form on the walls of the arteries. Research has shown that active people are less prone to heart disease and are less likely to die from a heart attack than inactive people.

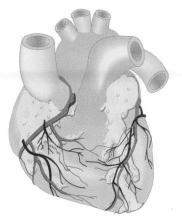

NORMAL CIRCULATION

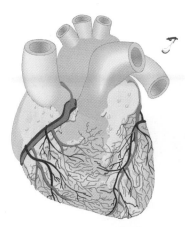

EXTRA VESSELS FROM EXERCISE

Research has shown that people who engage in regular exercise develop extra arteries in the heart muscle.

Everyone would like to have enough energy to take part in a favorite sport or recreational activity without feeling tired. One way to obtain additional energy is to increase the oxygen supply to muscles by exercising the heart. As you engage in cardiovascular activities, your heart muscle gets stronger and works more efficiently because it is able to pump out more blood with each beat. In addition, the trained heart beats fewer times per minute than the heart of someone who is not physically fit. The result is that the muscles receive more oxygen and do not tire as easily.

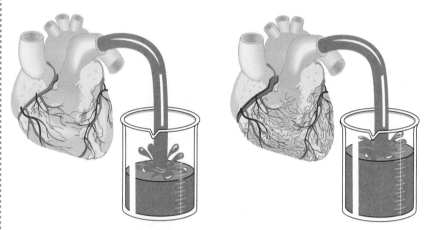

The active person's heart is able to pump out more blood with each beat.

Not only do you lessen your chances of developing heart disease and make your cardiovascular system more efficient through training, you also obtain mental benefits. Concentration, ability to cope with stress, and self-concept are improved.

APPLICATION OF TRAINING PRINCIPLES

The main purpose of any cardiovascular fitness program is to increase the body's ability to utilize oxygen. To increase cardiovascular fitness you must engage in exercises that involve movements of the large muscles of the body. You must be able to maintain these exercises continuously for at least 15 to 30 minutes. Such exercises are called aerobic because the working muscles continue to receive as much oxygen as they need. Brisk walking or jogging are activities that meet the above aerobic requirements.

Considerable research has led to the development of the principles of training. By following these principles, you will be able to train efficiently and avoid possible strain and injury.

PRINCIPLE OF OVERLOAD

One way to increase the oxygen supply to all muscles is to develop the muscle that serves as the pump. Since the heart is a muscle, it responds to training like other muscles.

To develop the heart muscle, you must push it beyond its normal range and make it pump more blood with each beat. This additional overload can be placed on the heart by an increase in the frequency, intensity, or time (duration) of the exercise program.

FREQUENCY

The exercise selected must be performed regularly to reach an adequate level of cardiovascular fitness. Ideally, your training program will become a daily habit; however, benefits can be achieved with fewer workouts.

Since the heart is a muscle, it can be made stronger just like any other muscle.

Bicycling is an aerobic activity and will develop cardiovascular fitness.

Aerobic activities must be performed at least three times per week to reach an adequate level of cardiovascular fitness.

As a beginner you may elect to walk, swim, or bike three days per week, then increase the overload by doing your selected activity four days, then five days, and finally on a daily basis. Participating in such activities two days per week will not significantly increase cardiovascular fitness. However, such a schedule may maintain the level you have acquired.

INTENSITY

In cardiovascular training you are trying to strengthen the heart and improve the body's ability to utilize oxygen. Although the heart is a muscle, you cannot observe it becoming stronger, as you can the biceps. Therefore, you must rely upon the pulse rate,

which is an external sign of the heart's condition since it corresponds exactly to the beat of the heart.

The intensity of a cardiovascular activity may be determined by the response of the pulse rate. How much should you increase the heart rate? If you do not increase it enough, little or no improvement in cardiovascular fitness will occur. On the other hand, exercising too hard too soon may cause extreme discomfort.

Each person has a **maximum heart rate** that should not be exceeded. To determine your maximum heart rate, subtract your age from 220. The Maximal Heart Rate Chart illustrates the maximal heart rate for various ages. Note that as you become older the maximal heart rate decreases.

To obtain the greatest cardiovascular benefits, the American College of Sports Medicine recommends that the intensity of your training be sufficient to increase your heart rate to a range of 60 to 90 percent of maximum heart rate or at 50 to 85% of heart rate reserve. The percent range of your heart rate while exercising is termed the **target heart rate** zone and is the desired level of intensity for most people.

There are two different methods you may use to calculate your target heart rate training zone. One is based on calculating a percentage of your maximum heart rate while the other is based on a percentage of your maximum heart rate reserve and takes into account your resting pulse rate. Each method has an advantage over the other. For example, while a percentage of the maximum heart rate method is easier to calculate, the maximum heart rate reserve method is more personalized since it takes into account your resting pulse rate. Both methods of calculating your target heart rate training zone are described below.

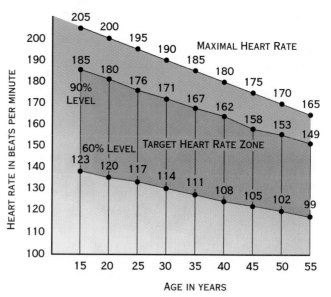

As age increases, maximum attainable heart rate decreases, thus affecting the upper and lower levels of the target heart-rate zone.

Both methods have minimum percentage limits. However, you should always start aerobic training at a lower percentage if you have not been active for some time or are overweight. While you will not obtain all of the benefits of aerobic training, some improvement will occur. For example, start at a 30 or 40 percent range and gradually progress to a 50 or 60 percent range.

Percentage of maximum heart rate (60 to 90 percent)

To compute your target heart rate zone using the percentage of maximum heart rate method, you must first determine your own maximum heart rate (220 − age = maximum heart rate). This value is multiplied by the lower percent at which you wish to train.

(220 − age) × 60% = lower level of target heart rate zone

The above formula should be used again to obtain the upper limit of your target heart rate zone. Substitute 90 percent in the formula in place of the 60 percent lower limit.

Below is an example of how Lunetta figured the lower and upper limits of her target heart rate zone. Lunetta is 14 years old and her resting heart rate is 70.

Percentage of Maximum Heart Rate Calculation		
	Lower Limit	Upper Limit
1. Lunetta subtracted 14 (age) from 220 to obtain her maximum heart rate of 206. 220 − age = maximum heart rate.	220 −14 206 MHR	220 −14 206 MHR
2. She decided that 60% should be the lower limit of her target heart rate zone and that 90% would be a safe upper limit for training effect.	× 60%	× 90%
3. She multiplied Step 2 times the value of Step 1. She determined that 123.6 was the lower limit of her target heart rate zone and 185.4 was the safe upper limit.	123.6	185.4

Percentage of heart rate reserve (50 to 85 percent)

7-2

To compute your target heart rate zone using the percentage of the heart-rate-reserve method, you must again first determine your own maximum heart rate (220 − age). Your resting heart rate is then subtracted from your maximum heart rate. This value is multiplied by the lower percent at which you wish to train and is added to the resting heart rate.

[(220 − age) − resting heart rate] × 50% + resting heart rate = lower level of target heart rate zone

The above formula should be used again to obtain the upper limit of your target heart rate zone. Eighty five percent would be substituted in the formula in place of the 50 percent lower limit.

Below is an example of how Chris figured the lower and upper limits of his target heart rate zone. Chris is 14 years old and his resting heart rate is 70.

Percentage of Maximal Heart Rate Reserve		
	Lower Limit	Upper Limit
1. Chris subtracted 14 (age) from 220 to obtain his maximum heart rate of 206. 220 − age = maximum heart rate.	220 − 14 206 MHR	220 − 14 206 MHR
2. Using the method described in this chapter, he determined his resting heart rate to be 70 which was subtracted from 206.	− 70 RHR 136	− 70 RHR 136
3. Chris decided that 50% should be the lower limit of his target heart rate zone and that 85% would be a safe upper limit for training effect	× 50%	× 85%
4. He multiplied Step 3 times the value of Step 2.	68	122.4
5. Chris then added his resting heart rate.	+ 70 RHR	+ 70 RHR
6. It was determined that 138 was the lower limit of his target heart rate zone and 186 was the safe upper limit.	138	185.6

Once the target heart rate zone is known, you will be able to check the intensity of your exercise by stopping briefly from time to time to count your pulse rate. Many people find it difficult to utilize this information, since they have to count their pulse for ten seconds and then multiply by six for a one-minute count (60 seconds). This may be hard to do if you are swimming in a pool or jogging two miles from home. A helpful hint: divide the lower and upper limits of your target heart rate zone by six. This will give you a ten-second count that can be easily remembered. For example, if your target heart rate lower limit is 151 and your upper limit is 192, divide both by six. The ten-second count would be 25 for the lower limit and 32 for the upper limit.

If your pulse falls below the lower limit of your target heart rate zone while you are exercising, you should increase your intensity (speed up your pace). If your pulse goes above the upper limit of your target heart rate zone, decrease your intensity (slow down your pace).

TIME

To achieve all the values of cardiovascular training, you must maintain the target heart rate (60 to 90 percent of your maximum heart rate or 50 to 85 percent of your maximum heart rate reserve) for a minimum of 20 minutes. A beginner may find it necessary to start a program involving less time and progressively increase the length of time of the exercise session.

To increase the overload, you may choose to increase the pace (intensity) or the distance (time) jogged. For example, after weeks of 20-minute exercise sessions in which you were steadily increasing your pace (intensity) to keep your pulse in the target heart rate zone, you might choose to increase your distance (time) and decrease your pace (intensity). Remember that as time is increased, intensity decreases.

Summary of Cardiovascular Endurance Training Guidelines

Frequency   Exercise at least 3 times per week.

Intensity   Work at 60 to 90% maximum heart rate.
                Work at 50 to 85% maximum heart rate reserve.

Time   Maintain continuous large muscle group activity for minimum of 20 minutes.

The chart below summarizes a typical aerobic exercise session for someone using a percentage of maximum heart rate to calculate their target heart rate training zone. As you will note, this individual has a normal heart rate of 70 beats per minute. After a five- to

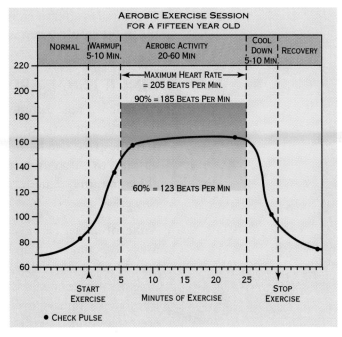

Heart rate during a typical aerobic exercise session

ten-minute warm-up, the individual gradually increases her heart rate to 130 beats per minute, which is at the lower level of the target heart rate zone. She slightly increases the heart rate and maintains it within the target heart rate zone of 124 to 185 beats per minute. This level of activity is maintained for 20 to 60 minutes. At the conclusion of the training period, she begins her cooldown session to gradually reduce the heart rate. After the cooldown, she begins the recovery stage, with the heart returning to its preactivity level.

PRINCIPLE OF PROGRESSION

Since the heart adjusts to the workload you place on it, the overload must be periodically increased in order for improvement to occur. For example, if you begin a regular exercise program that involves jogging one mile in nine minutes, you might find the workout stressful. Your cardiovascular fitness would gradually improve if you continued the nine-minute rate. But after several weeks of jogging the same distance in the same time, cardiovascular improvement would stop and adaptation would occur. To continue improving your cardiovascular fitness, you would have to increase the stress by jogging a mile in a shorter period of time. This progressive increase in the overload would place additional stress on your cardiovascular system and produce additional improvement.

Remember to observe your target heart rate and recovery heart rate. If, while training, your heart rate goes above or below your target heart rate zone, adjustments need to be made. Also, you need to reduce the intensity or duration of your training program if your recovery heart rate is not less than 120 beats per minute five minutes after exercising or not less than 100 beats per minute ten minutes after exercising.

PRINCIPLE OF SPECIFICITY

Aerobic exercise promotes cardiovascular fitness better than any other type of activity. **Aerobic** means *with oxygen* and involves activities that can be performed for at least 15 minutes without gasping to catch your breath. Examples of aerobic activities include jogging, dancing, swimming, bicycling, racquetball, and soccer.

7-3

Anaerobic (*without oxygen*) activity is performing at a pace which uses oxygen faster than the body can replenish it. Since this is true, anaerobic exercise can be done only for a short period of time. Examples would be the 220-yard dash or the 50-yard freestyle swimming events. What other events would be considered anaerobic? Aerobic?

7-4

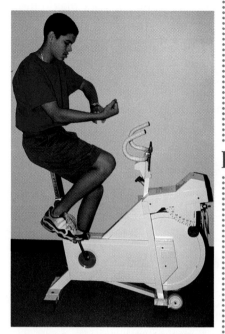

Monitoring your pulse will give you an indication whether you need to increase or decrease your intensity.

Below is a chart to help you set cardiovascular fitness goals. If after completing the mile run/walk you find that it took two minutes or more beyond the time established for your age and gender, this would be interpreted as "less" than the health fitness standard. If you fall within this category you may expect rapid improvement initially if you maintain a regular exercise routine. An appropriate cardiovascular goal would be to show improvement in the range from 30 seconds to five minutes, depending on how much you are motivated during the test. If you are close to or within two minutes of the health fitness standard, you should set six-month goals within a range of 15 to 90 seconds. If you exceed the health fitness standard, set improvement goals within a range of 0 to 45 seconds.

Cardiovascular Goal Setting			
	Distance from Health Fitness Standard		
	Less	Close	Exceeds
Difference Between Test Score and Health Fitness Standard	2 minutes+	0 to 2 minutes	0 or better
Recommended Range for Goals	30 seconds to 5 minutes	15 seconds to 90 seconds	0–45 seconds

SUMMARY

Cardiovascular fitness includes the efficient operation of the circulatory and respiratory systems. These systems improve with use and decline with disuse. Thus, the more active you are, the more energy you will have, and the more your chances of developing cardiovascular disease will decrease.

One important element of cardiovascular fitness is the efficiency of the heart, since it pumps oxygen-rich blood to the muscles. Because your heart is a muscle, it becomes stronger when exercised. Aerobic activities, such as swimming and jogging, will provide a training effect when maintained for a minimum of 15 minutes and performed at least three days per week.

You must rely on your pulse rate to determine the effect of training. By calculating your resting heart rate, target heart rate zone, and recovery heart rate, you will know where to begin. With careful monitoring during your training session, you will know when to progress.

Having a high level of energy is one of the most important benefits of exercise. Without energy, it is very hard to feel good about yourself. While following a sound cardiovascular fitness program may not always be easy, the payoff can be most rewarding. Here's to healthy hearts.

MULTIPLE CHOICE

Place the letter of the best answer in the space provided.

1. When you increase the pace of your run, you are increasing
   A. frequency. B. intensity. C. time. D. none of the above.

2. In order for jogging to contribute to the development of cardiovascular fitness, your target heart rate must be maintained for at least
   A. three minutes. B. five minutes. C. ten minutes. D. twenty minutes.

3. Which of the following is *not* a primary benefit of regular cardiovascular exercise?
   A. increased ability to take in oxygen   C. lower blood pressure
   B. improved balance   D. lower pulse rate

4. Which of the blood vessels have one-way valves?
   A. arteries B. capillaries C. veins D. both A and C

5. Blood flow in the body follows the pattern of
   A. heart to arteries to capillaries to veins.
   B. heart to arteries to veins to capillaries.
   C. heart to veins to arteries to capillaries.
   D. veins to capillaries to heart to arteries.

6. Your friend, who is age 15, wishes to start a jogging program. Using a percentage of maximal heart rate, what would you suggest as a proper starting target heart rate?
   A. 123 B. 146 C. 155 D. 178

7. What should your training heart rate be in order to safely develop cardiovascular fitness?
   A. 140 bpm B. 60 percent C. 95 percent D. 190 bpm

8. Which of the following is an appropriate cardiovascular fitness training activity?
   A. football B. 100-yard dash C. swimming D. weight lifting

9. The intensity of your workout is too difficult if your heart rate has not returned to 120 bpm within how many minutes?
   A. 2 minutes B. 5 minutes C. 10 minutes D. 15 minutes

10. What is the minimum number of days per week a person should exercise to improve cardiovascular fitness?
    A. one B. three C. five D. seven

DISCUSSION

11. How does cardiovascular fitness allow you to exercise longer?

12. What type of activities are best for developing cardiovascular fitness? Why?

13. You currently can jog one mile in 12 minutes, but you have a personal goal of jogging two miles in 20 minutes. How would you train to reach your goal?

14. Why should your pulse rate be taken after an exercise session?

15. Review the personal goals you developed in Chapter 3. Did any of your goals focus upon improvement of cardiovascular fitness? If not, develop a goal for cardiovascular fitness improvement.

MUSCULAR FITNESS

8

CHAPTER OBJECTIVES

As you read this chapter, look for answers to these key questions:

- What is the difference between muscular strength and muscular endurance?

- How does a weight-training program affect males and females differently?

- What three types of fibers are found in skeletal muscles?

- How can the training principles be applied to improve muscular strength and muscular endurance?

- What are the primary differences between muscular strength and muscular endurance training?

- What safety practices should you follow when lifting weights?

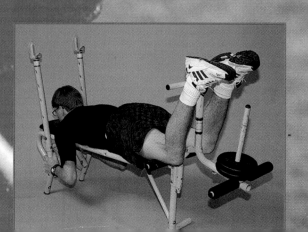

VOCABULARY

When you have completed this chapter, you should understand the meaning of these vocabulary terms:

- atrophy
- slow-twitch fibers
- intermediate-twitch fibers
- fast-twitch fibers
- isometric exercises
- isotonic exercises
- isokinetic exercises
- repetition
- resistance
- set

> The difference between successful people and others is not a lack of strength, not a lack of knowledge, but rather a lack of will.
>
> **VINCE LOMBARDI**

MUSCULAR STRENGTH AND ENDURANCE

Muscular fitness includes two health-related components of physical fitness: muscular strength and muscular endurance. Muscular strength is the ability of a muscle group to apply a maximal force against a resistance one time. The term resistance in weight training simply refers to the weight lifted. Muscular endurance is the ability to repeat muscle movement over a period of time.

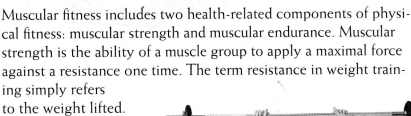

To look good and feel good, you must have adequate muscular fitness. Why do two people with the same weight and height but with different amounts of muscle and body fat look different? The person with more muscle looks trimmer because muscle is denser than fat. One pound of muscle takes up less space than one pound of fat. Another reason is that toned muscles prevent protruding in areas such as the abdomen.

Another factor influencing your appearance is good posture. Developing your body's muscles will help you have the strength and endurance to carry your body in an upright position. Good posture makes you look better. Do you know someone who does not stand up straight? Compare that person with someone who does.

Strong muscles not only improve your appearance, they also help you perform physical activity better. Additionally, strong muscles help to reduce fatigue, avoid back pain, and prevent muscle injuries and muscle soreness.

MYTHS ABOUT WEIGHT TRAINING

Some people may tell you that weight training makes a person muscle-bound or inflexible. Others say muscular fitness is good for men, but unfeminine for women. Still others tell you that muscles will turn into fat if you stop training. Of course, none of these myths is true.

MUSCLE-BOUND PHYSIQUE

Years ago body builders encouraged men to do exercises that often made them muscle-bound. Such individuals did not do flexibility exercises or perform their strength training exercises properly. As a result, they lost some of the range of motion in certain joints. Becoming muscle-bound is not a problem when weight-training exercises are performed properly.

IS WEIGHT TRAINING GOOD FOR FEMALES?

Those who believe strength training is good for males but not for females are wrong. Females have estrogen, rather than testosterone, as their primary sex hormone. This eliminates the chance of a female developing bulging muscles while training with weights. Females also should not be concerned about dramatic changes in muscle definition, since they have an average of eight percent more body fat than males, which masks muscle definition. A female can realize all the benefits of weight training without worrying about muscle bulk and definition. Good muscular fitness is just as important for women as it is for men, since both will appear more attractive when physically fit.

CAN MUSCLE TURN INTO FAT?

A major misconception about weight training is that muscle will turn into fat when you stop lifting weights. Muscle does not turn into fat, nor does fat turn into muscle. Muscle is muscle and fat is fat. What really happens is that muscles atrophy, or become smaller, when they are not used. Muscle atrophy can easily be seen when an arm becomes thinner after being placed in a cast for several weeks. An increase of fat will occur only if you continue to take in more calories than you burn.

Females will gain many benefits from a muscular fitness program.

MUSCLE FIBER COMPOSITION

There is about as much truth to fat turning into muscle as muscle turning into fat.

While muscular strength and endurance are closely related, they are separate components of health-related fitness. To understand how to apply the three principles of training to strength and endurance, you must first understand that different muscle fibers are involved in these two health-related components.

Skeletal muscles are attached to bones by tendons. When they contract or shorten, they produce movement. There are three types of skeletal muscle fibers, slow, intermediate, and fast-twitch. All three types of fibers are found in skeletal muscles. Heredity determines the number of slow, intermediate, and fast-twitch fibers you possess. However, you can improve both the fitness and performance level of each kind of fiber with appropriate exercises.

SLOW-TWITCH FIBERS

Slow-twitch fibers are also called red fibers because of the large amount of blood supply directed to them. Such fibers are slow to contract but have the ability to continue contracting for long periods of time. These fibers are best suited for aerobic or muscular endurance activities, since they do not tire easily. Slow-twitch fibers enable individuals to run long distances or repeat muscular tasks many times. It is because slow-twitch fibers contract slowly and do not tire easily that thousands of runners complete the Boston Marathon.

INTERMEDIATE-TWITCH FIBERS

Intermediate-twitch fibers possess a combination of fast and slow-twitch fiber characteristics. Specifically, intermediate-twitch fibers are capable of contracting at a faster speed than slow-twitch fibers but at a slower speed than fast-twitch fibers. In addition, fatigue occurs much more slowly in the intermediate-twitch muscle fibers than in the fast-twitch fiber.

FAST-TWITCH FIBERS

Another name for **fast-twitch fibers** is white fibers. These fibers contract quickly, allowing explosive muscular contractions and, therefore, lend themselves more readily to anaerobic, or strength related, activities. An example of a person who needs a large number of fast-twitch fibers is a sprinter. This athlete must react quickly to the sound of the starting pistol. Fast-twitch fibers fatigue easily.

As in strengthening the heart, a skeletal muscle becomes stronger when it works harder than it has been accustomed to working. Three types of exercises provide resistance to make the muscle work harder for the purpose of developing muscular fitness: isometric, isotonic, and isokinetic.

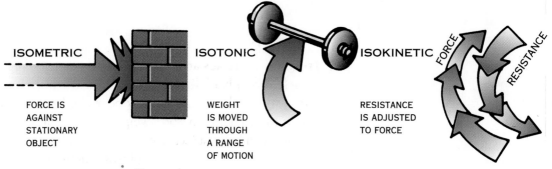

ISOMETRIC FORCE IS AGAINST STATIONARY OBJECT

ISOTONIC WEIGHT IS MOVED THROUGH A RANGE OF MOTION

ISOKINETIC RESISTANCE IS ADJUSTED TO FORCE

FORCE RESISTANCE

Types of resistance exercises

ISOMETRIC EXERCISES

In an **isometric exercise**, you contract, or tighten, your muscles but do not change their length. To perform an isometric exercise you push against a stationary object or against another part of your body that prevents movement. For example, place a tennis ball in your hand and squeeze it as hard as possible for a period of 6 to 8 seconds. Note that there is no movement of the body part (hand) or object (ball) against which the force is exerted.

Strength improvement will result from isometric contraction. However, it is developed only at the position the exercise is performed. Strength is not developed throughout the entire range of movement, which includes many possible positions. For example, if you are performing an isometric arm exercise, you will develop strength only at that specific angle. Your arm goes through many different angles when fully extending and flexing. It would be impossible to exercise all positions effectively utilizing isometric principles. Therefore, these exercises are the least effective in developing strength and endurance.

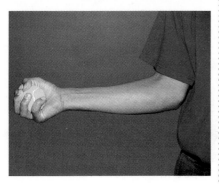

Grip strength can be improved through isometric exercises.

8-1

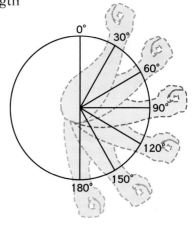

0° 30° 60° 90° 120° 150° 180°

During isometric contractions, strength is developed only at one fixed position within a muscle's full range of movement.

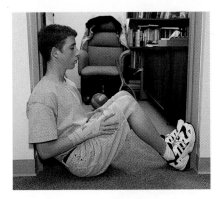

Isometric exercises may be used to develop strength when temporarily or permanently disabled.

Increase resistance by adding weights.

Isometric exercises can be hazardous for older persons or for those with high blood pressure and other circulatory ailments. Such exercises temporarily impair circulation of the blood and cause the blood pressure to rise. Also since isometrics provide no movement, muscular endurance and flexibility are not improved.

There are some advantages to doing isometric exercises. They require no special equipment and are useful for people with certain physical disabilities and people confined to a small space. For example, isometrics can be done while sitting at a desk or while riding in a car.

ISOTONIC EXERCISES

Isotonic exercises are those in which you lengthen and shorten the muscle through a full range of movement while lowering and raising a resistance. The resistance may be in the form of a barbell (weight training) or your own body weight (calisthenics). An isotonic contraction can be observed when you lift a glass of water to drink. The biceps muscle on the front of the arm contracts and shortens, causing the elbow to bend. To lower the glass, the biceps muscle relaxes and lengthens. Another example is when a barbell is raised and lowered through a muscle's full range of movement.

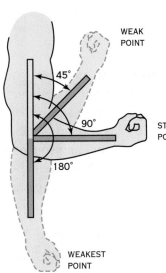

Strength varies according to the angle of the joint.

With isotonic exercise, the actual amount of weight the muscle is able to lift varies throughout the range of motion. The heaviest amount of weight lifted will be equal to the capacity of your limb at the weakest joint position throughout the total range of movement. For example, at a 90-degree joint angle you may be able to lift 80 pounds, while at a 160-degree angle you may be able to lift only 40 pounds. The 160-degree joint angle limitation means you will only be able to lift 40 pounds throughout the full range of motion. This amount of weight might not be sufficient to overload the strongest joint position. Despite this drawback, isotonic exercises are excellent muscular fitness developers.

ISOKINETIC EXERCISES

A muscle has different levels of strength while moving through a complete range of motion. In other words, the angle at which the muscle is pulling on the bone determines the amount of weight you can lift.

109

Isokinetic exercises, with the use of specially designed machines, overcome the disadvantages of isometric and isotonic exercises. The isokinetic machine mechanically allows you to overload a muscle with maximum resistance throughout the muscle's entire range of movement at a constant speed. The obvious advantage of this method is that maximum resistance is provided at the stronger angles, while less resistance is provided at the weaker angles.

Variable weight machines provide maximum resistance throughout the entire range of motion.

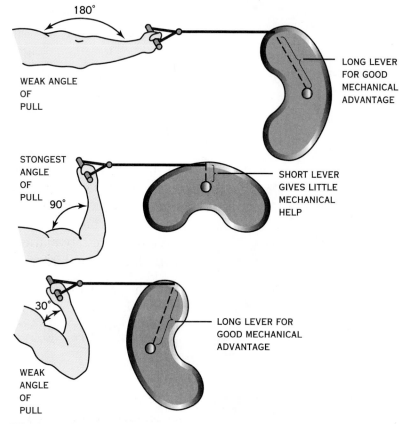

Weight machines with cams provide variable resistance through the full range of motion.

Currently, there are few truely isokinetic weight-training machines in fitness centers that provide both constant speed and constant resistance. Many fitness centers have, however, variable resistance weight machines which provide varying resistance throughout a complete range of motion. As the cable moves over the irregularly shaped cam, the resistance is adjusted in accordance with the lever characteristics of a specific joint movement.

APPLICATION OF TRAINING PRINCIPLES

The type of exercises and equipment you use influences the method in which you apply training principles to muscular strength and endurance development. Since isometric exercises have many disadvantages and isokinetic exercises require expensive equipment not readily available in the home, the application of training principles in this chapter is limited to the use of isotonic exercises.

Recall that fast-twitch fibers allow you to perform strength-related tasks, and slow-twitch fibers allow you to perform muscular endurance activities. Intermediate-twitch fibers help you to perform both types of activities. To develop these different types of muscle fibers, you can perform many of the same exercises. The primary difference in muscular strength and muscular endurance training lies in the amount of weight lifted and the number of times it is lifted.

PRINCIPLE OF OVERLOAD

To improve muscular fitness, you must deal with three factors. First you must stimulate the muscle. This is accomplished by placing an overload on the muscle, making it work harder than normal. The second factor is nutrition. In order for a muscle to grow, it must receive adequate nutrients, which will be discussed in the following chapter. After the muscle has been overloaded and given the necessary nutrients, the muscle must be given time to rest, which is the third factor necessary for muscle development.

As in the case with the other health-related components, overload can be placed on the body to increase muscular strength and endurance through the application of frequency, intensity, or time (FIT).

FREQUENCY

Once your muscles have been stimulated by some form of resistance, such as lifting weights, they must be given time to grow. You must spend sufficient time resting between training sessions to allow this growth to occur. Most authorities agree that 48 hours are required. Therefore, muscles should be exercised every other day, not every day.

Some weight lifters prefer to work out every day. They accomplish this by working different muscle groups on alternating days. For example, one day they may work the upper body and the next day work the muscles in the lower body.

INTENSITY

The intensity of a weight training program is called the **resistance** and is determined by the amount of weight you lift. While you must increase resistance to improve muscular strength and endurance, it is important to remember that the increase must be gradual.

The intensity or amount of weight you can lift to improve muscular strength should be 60 to 90 percent of what you can lift one

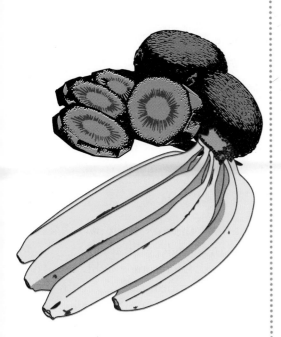

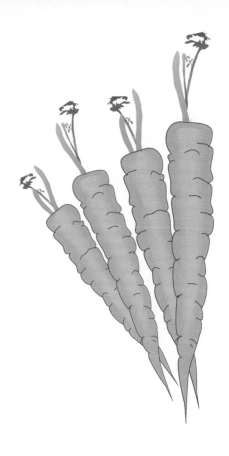

time. The amount of weight you can lift to improve muscular endurance should be 30 to 50 percent of what you can lift one time. For example, if you can lift 100 pounds one time and wish to improve muscular strength, you should train with a barbell weighing 60 to 90 pounds. If your intent is to improve muscular endurance, you should use a 30- to 50-pound barbell. It is generally accepted that exercising against a resistance more than 60 percent of your maximum is a form of strength training, and anything less than 60 percent is a form of endurance training. Beginners should always concentrate on endurance training in the early stages. By doing so, you will be able to control the weight resulting in excellent form and reduce the chances of muscle soreness.

Sample Workout Muscular Endurance Development							
Exercise	Goal	SET	Date				
			9-1	9-3	9-5	9-8*	9-10**
Front Curl	15 lbs. 20 reps.	1	15/12	15/16	15/20	15/20	20/18
		2	15/12	15/14	15/18	15/20	20/12
		3	15/12	15/14	15/18	15/20	20/12

Muscular Strength Development							
Exercise	Goal	SET	Date				
			9-1	9-3	9-5	9-8*	9-10**
Front Curl	40 lbs. 8 reps.	1	40/4	40/6	40/8	40/8	50/6
		2	40/4	40/6	40/6	40/8	50/4
		3	40/4	40/6	40/6	40/8	50/4

*goal achieved for all three sets
**weight increased, repetitions lowered

TIME

This refers primarily to the number of times the exercise is performed. A **repetition** is the completion of a single, full-range movement of the body part being exercised. Each time you lift a barbell or do a calisthenic exercise, you are performing one repetition. A group of repetitions performed one after the other is called a **set**. Usually, a person who is beginning a weight-training program performs three sets of repetitions with at least two minutes of rest between each set. To prevent muscle soreness, beginners should limit themselves to one set and gradually work up to two and three sets.

A. Muscular endurance—To develop muscular endurance, the resistance (intensity) should be low and the number of repetitions (time) high. Three sets of 12 to 20 repetitions need to be performed to qualify as a muscular endurance program.

B. Muscular strength—Whereas muscular endurance is developed with the use of light weights and many repetitions, muscular strength is developed with the use of heavy weights and few repetitions. Three sets of 4 to 8 repetitions need to be performed for maximum strength gain.

Summary of Muscular Fitness Training Guidelines	
Muscular Endurance	
Frequency	Every other day for each muscle group
Intensity	Low resistance (30 to 50% 1 RM)
Time	High repetitions (12 to 20 reps, 1 to 3 sets)
Muscular Strength	
Frequency	Every other day for each muscle group
Intensity	Heavy weights (60 to 90% 1 RM)
Time	Low repetitions (4 to 8 reps, 1 to 3 sets)

PRINCIPLE OF PROGRESSION

You now know you must overload muscles to improve muscular strength and endurance. Since your body adapts to lifting the same amount of weight, you must gradually lift more. If you try lifting too much too soon, you run the risk of muscle or joint injury.

You should perform three sets of 4 to 8 repetitions to improve muscular strength. Start with the maximum amount of weight you can lift four times for all three sets. If you cannot lift this amount four times during the third set, decrease the amount of weight. As you make progress and are able to lift the amount of weight eight times for all three sets, add additional weight and drop your number of repetitions back to four per set. To improve muscular endurance, use the same approach with less weight and more repetitions (12 to 20 per set).

PRINCIPLE OF SPECIFICITY

You must overload the specific muscle you want to improve. If you want to increase leg strength, you must do leg exercises. You will not improve your leg strength by doing arm exercises. The more you can target or isolate the muscle you want to improve, the better the results.

To achieve the best results, select the appropriate exercise and place your body and/or body part in a certain position to isolate the muscle. This will force the targeted muscle to do the intended work rather than having the work spread over a number of secondary muscle movers. The standing biceps curl is a good example of how to isolate a muscle group. By standing next to a wall, you can greatly reduce the influence of the legs and hips, forcing the biceps to do the work. This technique results in more strength being gained in the targeted area.

Your weight training program must be designed to meet your specific needs and goals. You will have to design a specific program to achieve specific results regardless of whether you are trying to improve strength, add bulk, improve muscle tone, or lose weight.

The American College of Sports Medicine recommends resistance training that is of moderate intensity, sufficient to develop and maintain fat-free weight. They also recommend at least one set of from 8 to 12 repetitions of eight to ten exercises that work the major muscle groups at least two days per week.

GOAL SETTING FOR ABDOMINAL STRENGTH AND ENDURANCE

Abdominal strength is one of the components of health-related physical fitness that can be improved fairly rapidly if a person appropriately applies the training principles and the variables of overload. However, this component cannot be improved as rapidly as cardiovascular and flexibility components. Therefore, short-term goals for individuals whose test scores fall within the category of substantially "less" than the standard should be established carefully. If your sit-up test score is 15 or more below the

Performing curl against wall to target biceps

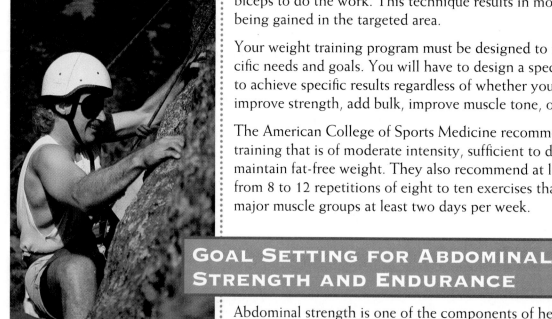

Principles of training apply to everyone, regardless of disability.

health fitness standard you should set six-month improvement goals to improve from 5 to 15 sit ups. If your test score falls in the category of "close" to the standard, set your goal for a range of improvement of from 2 to 10 sit-ups. If you "exceed" the health fitness standard, set your goal to improve from 1 to 4 sit-ups.

Goal Setting for Abdominal Strength and Endurance			
	Distance from Health Fitness Standard		
	Less	Close	Exceeds
Difference Between Test Score and Health Fitness Standard	More than 15	1 to 15	0 or better
Recommended Range for Goals	5 to 15	2 to 10	1 to 4

GOAL SETTING FOR UPPER BODY STRENGTH

Upper body strength is one of the components of health-related physical fitness that can be improved if a person appropriately applies the training principles and the overload variables. Strength components of physical fitness cannot be improved as rapidly as cardiovascular and flexibility components. Therefore, short-term goals for individuals whose test score is initially within the category of substantially "less" than the standard should be established carefully. It is better to set goals low and have to revise them upward than to set them too high and have to revise them downward. If your pull-up test score is zero, or more than 2 below the health fitness standard, you should set six-month improvement goals to improve 1 to 3 pull-ups. If your test score falls in the category of "close" to the standard, set goals with a range of improvement of 2 to 5 pull-ups. If you "exceed" the health fitness standard, you should set your goal to improve 1 to 3 pull-ups.

Goal Setting for Upper Body Strength			
	Distance from Health Fitness Standard		
	Less	Close	Exceeds
Difference Between Test Score and Health Fitness Standard	More than 1	1–2	at or better
Recommended Range for Goals	1–3	2–5	1–3

Regardless of the type of training program, safety should always be a major consideration. When engaging in weight training programs, you should always take precautions to reduce the risk of injury. One of the most important precautions is to train with a partner, who can serve as a spotter and keep you from being pinned under a weight. You should also take the following precautions.

1. Warm up properly before you begin any physical conditioning program.

2. Concentrate on endurance when beginning a weight training program. The lighter weights will give you an opportunity to learn how to perform the exercises correctly. The endurance training will prepare your body for higher intensity strength training.

3. Check barbell plates before you lift to make sure they are properly secured and will not slip off.

4. Keep hands dry for a good grip.

5. Hold the bar or machine handgrips comfortably, since a tight grasp may cause your blood pressure to increase.

6. Exhale when pushing against the resistance (blow the weight up) and inhale when lowering the weight. Holding your breath will cause a dramatic increase in your blood pressure and may damage some blood vessels. Although people argue about the correct way to breathe, the most important consideration is not to hold your breath.

7. Use correct form at all times to prevent injury and to achieve the greatest gains from the exercise. Reduce the weight if you cannot maintain control during the exercise.

8. Keep the weight close to the body when lifting it from the floor to your chest.

9. Space your feet a shoulder-width apart to provide balance and to help spread the load of the weight.

10. Keep the back straight, with hips aligned below the shoulders. This will help prevent straining the back muscles.

11. Go through the complete range of motion to increase flexibility.

12. Exercise large muscle groups first, then the smaller groups.

13. Exercise muscles on both sides of the joint to ensure muscle balance.

14. Lift the weight on a count of two. Lower it more slowly on a count of four.

Tighten barbell collars before lifting.

15. Always do lifts or exercises in the same sequence from workout to workout. In this way, fatigue will be relatively the same at various points throughout the workout.

16. Do not perform the bench press or other lifts unless spotters are present. If you lose control without a spotter present, you could be pinned under the weight.

17. Avoid a deep-knee bend or full-squat position when performing exercises. You will lessen the chance of knee injury and achieve good results by doing the exercise with one-half knee bends.

MUSCULAR FITNESS EXERCISES

SHOULDERS

The following exercises primarily develop the muscles of the shoulder region.

Standing lateral raise

Shoulder shrug

STANDING LATERAL RAISE

Stand erect with feet spread shoulder width apart. Grasp a 5- to 10-pound dumbbell in each hand with palms inward. Raise the dumbbells sideways to a position directly overhead. Keep the arms straight throughout. Return to starting position and repeat.

SHOULDER SHRUG

Stand straight holding the barbell in front of the upper thighs, arms straight, using an overhand grip with hands close together. Shrug shoulders as if trying to touch your ears. Return to starting position and repeat.

Upright rowing

UPRIGHT ROWING

Stand erect, holding the barbell in front of the thighs with overhand grip and hands close together. Pull the bar to chin level while bending the elbows completely, keeping elbows higher than hands. Lower to starting position and repeat.

ARMS

The following exercises develop the muscles of the arms and hands.

PUSH-UPS

Lay face down on the floor and place the hands under your shoulders with the fingers pointing straight ahead. Push your body weight up until the arms are straight. Try to maintain a straight line from your shoulders to your heels. Lower your body by bending your arms until they form a 90 degree angle. Additional intensity may be gained by raising one or both legs. The higher the legs are raised (adding body weight), the greater the intensity.

Push-up

KNEE PUSH-UPS

Lay face down on the floor and place the hands under your shoulders with the fingers pointing straight ahead. Raise upper body off the floor by extending arms until you are supported only by hands and knees. Keep the body in a straight line from the head to the knees. Lower your body by bending your arms until they form a 90 degree angle.

Knee push-ups

Pull-up

Negative pull-ups

PULL-UPS

Grasp a horizontal bar with hands facing away from the body and shoulder width apart. Hang from the bar with extended arms and straight body. Pull chin above the bar without kicking; then lower to starting position. Repeat the movement as many times as possible.

NEGATIVE PULL-UP

Step on a chair or bench and assume the pull-up position with the chin above the bar. As you remove the feet from the support, lower your body as slowly as possible.

FRONT CURL

Hold the bar with palms facing out. Lift weight forward and upward, bending arms completely. Lower to starting position with arms fully extended before repeating. No other motion should be allowed with elbows or back.

Front curl

REVERSE CURL

Execute in the same manner as a front curl but use a reverse grip in which the palms face the body.

Reverse curl

TWO-ARM PRESS

Stand erect holding the barbell in front of the chest with palms facing forward while pressing the weight above the head until the arms are straight. Lower the weight and repeat.

Two-arm press

TRICEPS PRESS (FRENCH CURL)

This exercise is the same as the triceps extension except that you use a barbell to exercise both arms. The back should be straight with barbell held overhead and palms facing forward 8 to 12 inches apart. Lower the weight to the neck and repeat.

Triceps press (French curl)

WRIST CURLS

Grasp the dumbbell using an underhand grip. Sit and support your forearm on your thigh. Use the other hand to stabilize the wrist doing the curl. Raise and lower the weight by curling hands and wrists.

Wrist curls

REVERSE WRIST CURL

This movement is performed in the same way as the wrist curl, except that an overhand grip is used.

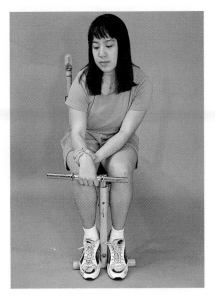

Reverse wrist curl

CHEST

The following exercises primarily develop the muscles of the chest region.

BENCH PRESS

Lie face up on the bench. With the arms in the extended position lower the bar to the chest and return to the extended position. CAUTION: Spotters should always be used for this exercise in case you get pinned under the weight.

Bench press

FLIES

Lie face up on the bench with knees bent and feet flat on the floor. Hold a weight in each hand (palms inward). Slowly lower the weights until the arms are parallel to the floor. Keeping the arms straight, raise the weights until they touch above you.

Flies

ONE-ARM RAISING

Place your right hand and right knee on the bench. Lift the weight upward to side of the chest, pause, then lower to starting position. Repeat with the right arm by placing your left hand and left knee on the bench.

One-arm raising

BACK

The following exercises primarily develop the muscles of the back region.

UPPER BACK LIFT

Lay face down with hands under your chin. Raise your chest off the floor by arching the upper back. Stop when your chest is off the floor. Return to starting position and repeat.

Upper back lift

KNEELING KNEE TUCK

Kneel with hands placed under the shoulders. Pull the knee of one leg toward your nose, then extend it horizontally. Repeat with the other leg.

Kneeling knee tuck

ABDOMINALS

The following exercise primarily develops the muscles of the abdominal region.

BENT-KNEE SIT-UPS (CURL-UP)

Lie flat on your back with arms folded across your chest and hands touching opposite shoulders. Bend your knees at a 90-degree angle. Your heels should be 12 to 18 inches from the buttocks. Curl up to a sitting position first with the head, then the shoulders, and finally the back. Uncurl and return to starting position. You may progressively increase the number of repetitions (time) and/or the resistance (intensity) by holding a weight on the chest or by lying head downward on an incline board.

Bent-knee sit-up

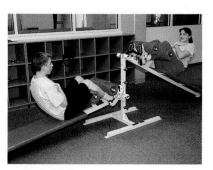

Sit-up using incline board

THIGHS

The following exercises primarily develop the muscles of the thigh region.

SIDE LEG LIFTS

Lie on your left side and raise your right foot upward. Lie on your right side and repeat with left leg. A freezer bag filled with beans or leg weights may be used to provide added resistance.

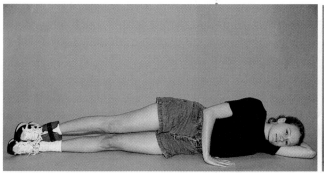

Side leg lifts

HALF-KNEE BENDS

Beware of doing full squats because knee injury can result. To begin the lift, stand straight with feet parallel and shoulder width apart and with barbell resting across the shoulders. You may wish to wrap a towel around the bar if it is too uncomfortable on the shoulders. Keeping the back straight, squat to one-half knee bend and return to the starting position. Heels should maintain contact with the floor at all times.

Half-knee bends

LEG EXTENSION

Sit on the end of a bench with ankles under the padded bar. Extend legs until they are straight and slowly return to the starting position.

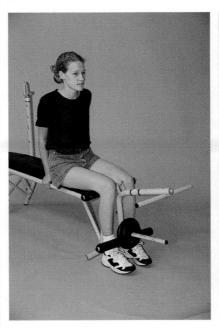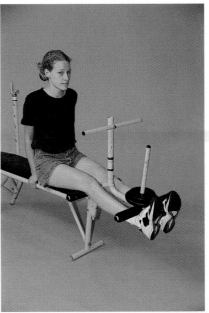

Leg extension

HAMSTRING CURL

Lay face down on a bench with ankles hooked under the padded bar. Flex your knees to a 90-degree angle and slowly return to the starting position.

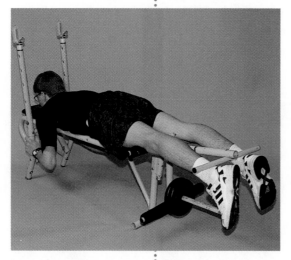 

Hamstring curl

CALF

The following exercise primarily develops the muscles of the calf region.

HEEL RAISER

Stand straight, feet parallel and toes elevated on a board with a barbell resting across shoulders. Supporting yourself on the balls of the feet, raise the heels as high as possible off the floor and then lower the heels to the starting position.

Heel raiser

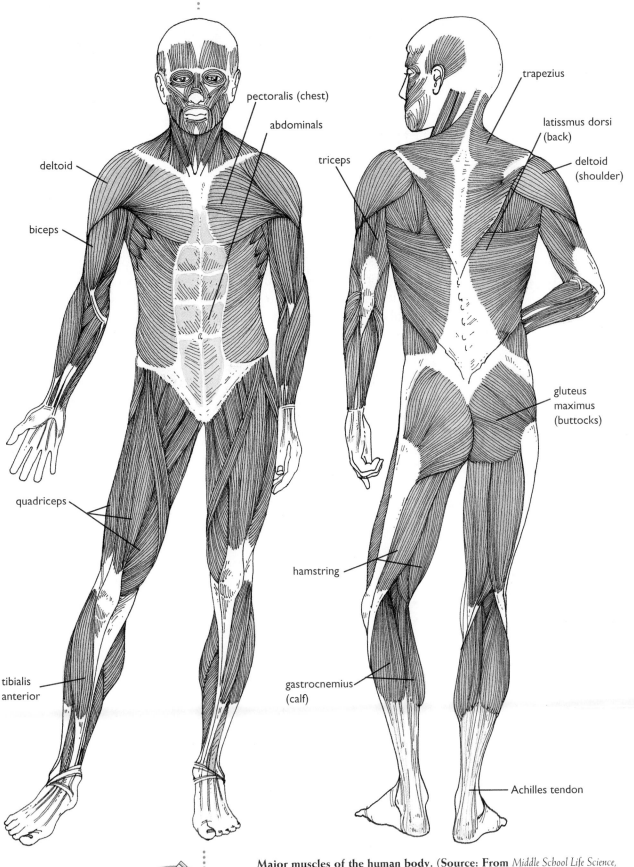

deltoid

biceps

quadriceps

tibialis
anterior

pectoralis (chest)

abdominals

trapezius

latissmus dorsi
(back)

deltoid
(shoulder)

triceps

gluteus
maximus
(buttocks)

hamstring

gastrocnemius
(calf)

Achilles tendon

Major muscles of the human body. (Source: From *Middle School Life Science*,
1st edition by Judy Capra, p. 187. Copyright © 1991 by Jefferson
County Public Schools, Golden, Colorado. Printed with permission.)

SUMMARY

There are many benefits to be derived from muscular fitness. You not only become stronger and reduce fatigue, but you also avoid muscular soreness and injuries.

Both males and females can benefit from muscular strength and endurance exercises. Females need not be concerned about developing bulky muscles because they have different hormones and a larger percent of body fat than males. Remember that fat is fat and muscle is muscle, and muscle can never turn into fat.

There are three types of skeletal muscle fibers. Slow-twitch or red fibers provide the body with the ability to do muscular endurance or aerobic activities. Intermediate-twitch fibers have characteristics of both slow-twitch and fast-twitch. Fast-twitch or white fibers enable the body to do muscular strength or anaerobic activities.

While muscular strength and muscular endurance are closely related, they are separate components of fitness. The primary difference in training for the two components is in the amount of weight and number of times a resistance is lifted.

STUDY QUESTIONS

TRUE-FALSE

Circle "T" for all correct statements and "F" for all incorrect ones.

T   F   1.   Muscle turns into fat when you stop a weight training program.

T   F   2.   The number of times you exercise per week determines the number of fast-twitch and slow-twitch fibers you have.

T   F   3.   Isometric exercises are recommended for an older person or those with high blood pressure, since they involve no heavy lifting.

T   F   4.   Isokinetic exercises require the use of expensive machines.

T   F   5.   You should lift heavy weights a few repetitions during each training session to develop muscular strength.

T   F   6.   You should perform your lifts in the same sequence from workout to workout.

T   F   7.   You should hold your breath when lifting a weight and breathe in when lowering it.

T   F   8.   The person with more muscle looks trimmer because muscle is denser than fat, thus taking up less space than fat.

T   F   9.   Females do not develop bulging muscles or experience muscle definition as males do because of testosterone, which is the female primary sex hormone.

T   F   10.   The difference in muscular strength and muscular endurance training is in the amount of weight lifted and the number of times it is lifted.

DISCUSSION

11.   Why should females not be concerned about developing bulging muscles?

12.   Briefly discuss the differences between isometric, isotonic, and isokinetic exercises. Which ones are you most likely to perform?

13.   Explain how the training techniques of muscular strength and muscular endurance development differ.

14.   Identify five precautions that will reduce the injury risk of weight training.

15.   Review the personal goals you developed in Chapter 3. Did any of your goals focus upon improvement of muscular fitness? If not, develop a goal for improvement of your muscular fitness.

NUTRITION

9

CHAPTER OBJECTIVES

As you read this chapter, look for answers to these key questions:

- How did you develop your current nutritional habits?

- What is the relationship of food to health?

- What are the essential nutrients and why does the body need them?

- What are the health problems that might occur from bad diet decisions about essential nutrients?

- Why is water such an important element of our diet?

- What is the new Food Label, and how can it help you plan a nutritionally balanced diet?

- What is the Food Guide Pyramid?

- How should the Food Guide Pyramid be used to plan a balanced diet?

- How should you determine your daily calorie requirements?

VOCABULARY

When you have completed this chapter, you should understand the meaning of these vocabulary terms:

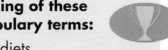

- fad diets
- proteins
- carbohydrates
- saturated fats
- unsaturated fats
- HDL
- LDL
- minerals
- fat-soluble vitamins
- water-soluble vitamins
- Food Guide Pyramid
- basal metabolism

Both males and females want to have a good physique, clear complexion, and glossy hair. Teenagers are especially interested in physical fitness and the ability to compete in athletic contests. None of these goals can be achieved without good health, and good health cannot be separated from good nutrition. To be in good health means that you feel like doing the things you want to do, such as racing a friend across the pool, skiing on the slopes, or merely getting through a hectic day. When one has plenty of vigor and vitality, second thoughts are not given to the energy required to achieve a desired task. Keeping yourself in a condition that enables you to meet daily situations cheerfully and eagerly is what nutrition is all about.

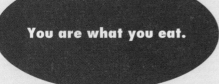

You are what you eat.

Sound nutrition is important if you want to lead an active, enjoyable lifestyle.

HISTORICAL USE OF FOOD

The original need for food was for survival only. In ancient times, nearly all of the human's day was spent searching for food by hunting, fishing, or scavenging. Later, when we learned to raise and store food supplies, food was used as the centerpiece of social and religious ceremonies. Today, we use food in a variety of ways including supplying our bodies with the essential nutrients. For example, food is used during social occasions, fellowship with friends, or as an escape when we are disappointed, sad, or depressed. Many of the ways we utilize food do not contribute to a balanced and nutritional diet and may lead to dietary problems.

ACQUIRED EXPERIENCES WITH FOOD

Why do you choose the foods you eat? Why do you like one food while your best friend likes another? Have you ever stopped to think why you and your family do not eat the type of food that other people eat, such as food that is popular in another country? Most people select the type of food they eat with little thought. You may want a pizza or a cheeseburger, but why do you choose them rather than some other foods? We eat and like the foods included in our diet for many reasons. The strongest factor is probably our family. We tend to eat and like what our family eats and likes. We have been eating foods our families prepares since our birth and have been conditioned to like it without having the opportunity to make decisions about those foods.

In addition to family influences, our friends and ethnic background are also strong factors that determine the food content of

Your ethnic background has a strong influence on your nutritional decisions.

our diets. When you grow older and change your family situation, you will have the opportunity to make your own decisions about what and how you eat. When you go to college, you will make new friends who like foods that you have never eaten before. Your friends will try to get you to taste some foods they like. Perhaps some of your new friends will be from different ethnic backgrounds and will help you develop a broader appreciation of different foods.

Lifestyle also determines what you eat. Are you rushed to get from school to soccer practice, or a music lesson, or a game? Think about how a busy lifestyle affects what you eat. Fast foods were developed for people who do not have a lot of time to make their own meals. The microwave is another invention that affects what we eat, since we may be too busy to take time to cook.

Other factors such as the cost of food, advertisements, the region of the country you live in, or your religious preference all have some influence on the type of foods you eat. You need to be sure that these factors are not influencing you to eat just one type of food. You can hold on to your ethnic or religious traditions and still maintain a balanced diet.

FOOD AND ITS RELATION TO HEALTH

"You are what you eat" is an old saying that may not be far from the truth. Food and how you relate to it has a great impact on your lifestyle. What do you think of when you hear the word *food*? Perhaps you think of your favorite meal or your favorite snack. Perhaps you think of social events and having fun. But do you think of fuel? Food is the fuel that keeps your body going. Food is the energy source for an active, vigorous, and fun lifestyle. If you do not eat enough of this energy source in the right proportions, you may not have the energy needed to enable you to be active.

Too much food leads to health problems associated with being too heavy. Also, if you eat too much food high in cholesterol or other fats, these foods may cause health problems. Health problems may also occur if your diet lacks one or more of the essential nutrients described later in this chapter. Having clear skin is a common goal for most teenagers. Many complexion problems are caused by an imbalance of chemicals in the body, and a balanced diet may be able to help.

Nutrition effects the way your hair, teeth, and skin look.

Diets that promote weight loss without establishing sound nutritional practices are considered **fad diets**. Health problems occur with many of the fad diets that you see on television or read about in the newspapers. Individuals have become seriously ill by depriving their body of essential nutrients over a long period of time because of a "special diet." No diet can cause a person to lose weight unless the caloric expenditure is greater than the caloric intake. A negative caloric balance forces the body to draw on energy stores for metabolism and jeopardises health by eliminating essential nutrients. Fad diets that restrict one's intake to one food, such as eggs or rice, are harmful. No one food contains all the nutrients necessary for a healthy lifestyle. Even milk, the one nearly perfect food, is low in iron and other nutrients. Good nutritional status requires that the proper balance and quantities of essential nutrients be obtained from a mixed diet of many possible food combinations.

ESSENTIAL NUTRIENTS

Your body needs certain essential nutrients to function properly. These nutrients are carbohydrates, fats, protein, minerals, and vitamins. Adequate amounts of each of these nutrients in your diet is essential for good health and your ability to maintain a balanced exercise program. The food you eat is the primary source for your essential nutrients. Many people take vitamins and other dietary supplements, but most of us could save that money if we ate a balanced diet.

PROTEINS

If you do not have a sufficient amount of carbohydrates in your diet, your body will use proteins for energy rather than for muscle building.

Proteins are the building blocks of the body and are extremely important when you are considering exercise to build muscle. Protein is present in every cell of the body. The most important function of protein is its role in the growth and repair of the body's tissues. Protein can also supply energy when there are not enough carbohydrates or fats in the diet. Foods in the meat group are the main dietary source of protein.

PROTEIN IS MADE OF AMINO ACIDS

Protein is made up of chemical substances known as **amino acids**. Amino acids are essential in the digestive process. Twenty-one amino acids have been identified. The body is able to make some amino acids from other food sources, but there are at least nine amino acids that cannot be manufactured in the body. These are referred to as **essential amino acids**. Essential amino acids must be included in your diet, with meats and animal products being the primary source. Soybeans are also an excellent source of

amino acids. If you decide not to eat red meat or animal products, your diet can still be balanced to contain all of the essential amino acids by including a mixture of the right beans, peas, nuts, and seeds. However, this balance is much harder to achieve, and a few vegetarians experience health problems because they are not careful enough about getting the right mixture.

ANIMAL PROTEIN

Complete proteins include such animal products as meat, milk, and eggs. These animal products contain an excellent balance of amino acids required for a healthy diet. In the United States and Canada, animal products are a staple food source, and there are few examples of individuals suffering from a lack of protein in their diet.

NON-MEAT PROTEIN

In many parts of the world, protein is obtained from dried beans or rice rather than animal products. Since these are not good sources of the essential amino acids, it is not uncommon to see many cases of stunted growth, underweight, slow recovery from illness, lack of vitality, and a lack of muscle tone.

CARBOHYDRATES

Carbohydrates serve as the "fuel" for our active, vigorous lifestyle and are obtained from breads, cereals, fruits, and concentrated sweets. They are the perfect source of energy. Carbohydrates can be used by the body easily and quickly. The body uses them first, before fats or proteins. Many teenagers as well as athletes give up carbohydrates in an attempt to lose weight. When teenagers eliminate carbohydrates, they usually have problems developing strength or muscle bulk even when they are eating a large quantity of protein. In other words, eliminating carbohydrates from the diet forces the body to use protein for fuel, instead of using the protein for body building.

STARCHES AND SUGARS

There are two types of carbohydrates, starches and sugar. Glucose is blood sugar and is the primary source of energy for the cells of the body. Have you ever become light-headed when you have not eaten for a while? That happened because you experienced low blood sugar, and your brain tissues were hungry or were being deprived of their fuel supply.

Starchy carbohydrates such as bread, potatoes, and cereals provide a good source of energy and contain a variety of nutrients. Sugary carbohydrates, like those found in soft drinks and candy, have few, if any, nutrients and are called empty calorie foods. Fruit and fruit juices are the best way of getting additional sugar into

Carbohydrates are the most efficient fuel for your body.

your diet because they contain other essential nutrients that the body needs.

FIBER

The undigestible material that makes up the walls of plant cells is known as fiber. Fiber is another kind of carbohydrate. Fiber is useful in moving waste through the body system and helpful in lowering the risk of certain diseases, including colon cancer. Common sources of fiber include whole grain breads and cereals, fruits, and vegetables. As you increase the fiber content of your diet, you should also increase your fluid intake. However, fiber should not be viewed as the cure-all of nutrition. Adding fiber to a nutritionally poor diet will not enhance the diet and may even have an adverse effect.

FATS

Fat stores twice as much energy as protein or carbohydrates but is not as easy to convert to energy as carbohydrates. Foods containing fat are divided into two major groups—*animal fats and vegetable fats*. Animal fats have a high **saturated fat** content and are found in meat, poultry, milk, cheese, ice cream, and egg yolks. Vegetable fats are **unsaturated fats** and are found in margarine, salad dressing, mayonnaise, cooking oils, avocados, olives, and nuts. Saturated and unsaturated fats are important because of their effects on the cholesterol level in the blood.

CHOLESTEROL

Cholesterol is a wax-like fatty substance that is produced by the body in the liver and used for building cells. In healthy people, the body produces all of the cholesterol that is needed. However, when you eat animal products high in saturated fats such as meat, cheese and eggs, you consume additional cholesterol. Cholesterol is transported throughout the body in the blood stream with excess amounts stored on the walls of the blood vessels. Excessive amounts of cholesterol in the circulatory system require storage and results in blocked arteries that limit blood flow to the brain and heart.

HDL AND LDL

There is both good cholesterol and bad cholesterol. The good type is called **HDL** (high density lipoprotein) while the bad type is called **LDL** (low density lipoprotein). It is believed that HDL helps remove the extra cholesterol from artery walls while LDL leads to the buildup of cholesterol on the artery walls. Cholesterol levels of greater than 180–200 places a person in danger of developing blocked blood vessels. Although the total amount of cholesterol in the blood is related to health dangers, the real concern is

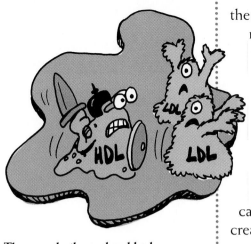

There are both good and bad cholesterol. The "good" HDLs are the body's police that help remove the "bad" LDLs from the blood stream.

the ratio of HDL to total cholesterol. Your goal should be to have no more than three times the amount of bad cholesterol (LDL) than you have good cholesterol (HDL).

The amount of total cholesterol in the body is closely related to diet, heredity, and regular vigorous exercise. It is believed that regular vigorous exercise and heredity are the major factors in determining the amount of HDL that you have in your blood. HDL helps remove cholesterol from the blood, so you want to do everything possible to develop HDL. There are no foods that contain HDL. Therefore, you can increase the ratio of HDL to LDL only by exercising and decreasing your intake of saturated fats.

MINERALS

When someone says your body needs **minerals**, you probably think of minerals found in the ground. In truth, the minerals needed by the body are taken from the ground. This is accomplished by eating plants or animals who have eaten plants.

There are twenty minerals present in the body that are used in body functions. Each of these is needed (in a very small amount) or serious deficiencies and diseases may occur. Like vitamins, minerals have no calories and provide no energy. They are important in regulating various bodily functions. Adequate mineral intake is necessary for good health. In general, those who eat a sound diet do not need a mineral supplement. Excessive mineral intake can be harmful.

Calcium and phosphorus are used in the development of bones and teeth as well as in muscular development. They are also used in the work of the muscles and the nervous system. Milk is a food rich in calcium.

Iron is combined with protein to form hemoglobin, an essential element of the blood. Good sources of iron are meats, green leafy vegetables, apricots, prunes, whole-grain and enriched cereals.

Iodine is essential for proper functioning of the thyroid. This mineral is available in iodized salt, sea food, and in fruits and vegetables grown in soil along sea coasts.

Potassium helps to maintain heartbeat, water balance, nerve transmission, and the breakdown of carbohydrates and proteins.

Sodium is a mineral that helps the body maintain a proper balance of body fluid. It plays a major role in nerve transmission, cardiac function, and normal metabolism. However, excessive amounts of sodium may lead to abnormal fluid retention which is related to hypertension. A balanced diet normally provides all of the sodium that you need.

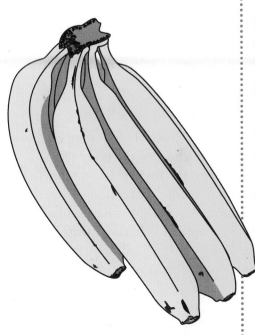

VITAMINS

Vitamins are organic, chemical substances found in very small amounts in food. You need only small amounts for normal growth and maintenance of the body. They do not supply energy but aid in utilization and absorption of nutrients. For example, the body requires vitamins in order to use carbohydrates, fats, and proteins for energy. Sometimes several vitamins work in combination with one another for a specific body reaction, and the absence of one of these needed vitamins prohibits the reaction from occurring. One vitamin cannot be substituted for another. All vitamins can be dissolved. Some are soluble in fat and some in water.

Many people waste money on vitamin supplements. A balanced diet provides the required vitamins for most people.

FAT-SOLUBLE VITAMINS

Some vitamins can be stored in fat deposits of the body and are called **fat-soluble vitamins**. It is critical that you do not take large supplemental doses of these vitamins, since an oversupply stored in the body could cause toxicity. The most important fat-soluble vitamins include Vitamin A, Vitamin D, Vitamin E, and Vitamin K.

WATER-SOLUBLE VITAMINS

Many vitamins that our body requires for proper functioning dissolve in water and, therefore, cannot be stored in the body tissue as the fat-soluble vitamins can be. When the body takes in more than it can use immediately, the extra vitamin is excreted in the urine. These vitamins must be consumed in our diet on a regular basis. You should be careful in food preparation because **water-soluble vitamins** dissolve in the liquid used in food preparation.

Water-soluable vitamins are lost when foods are cooked and the liquid is poured down the drain.

If you throw away those liquids, you will lose the vitamins. You should limit the amount of water used in cooking, and then try to incorporate that liquid into the meal. Overcooking also destroys the vitamin content in foods.

CONSUMER CONCERNS REGARDING VITAMINS

Advertisements in the media push the idea that multi-vitamin pills and mineral concentrates are needed by nearly everyone to make up for the lack of nutrients in modern processed foods or the lack of time for eating three balanced meals a day. The simple truth is that many vitamins cannot be stored by the body, and any taken in excess will simply be excreted in the urine. If the ones that can be stored are taken in large doses, toxicity may result. The good life cannot be gained from a bottle of vitamins.

BALANCED APPROACH TO VITAMINS

The best approach to providing the body with the proper amount of vitamins is by eating a balanced diet. If a person is deficient in a particular vitamin, a balanced diet will not correct the situation, and supplements may then have to be taken. In such cases, however, a physician should be consulted.

WATER: AN ESSENTIAL ELEMENT

Water is essential for your body and makes up about 65 percent of your weight. Although you may not think of water as a nutrient, it is essential for the normal functioning of the body. You can live longer without food than without water, for water is the primary component of blood and tissue fluids.

Water carries dissolved waste products from the body, helps digest food, and carries nutrients throughout the body. It also is critical to temperature control. When you perspire heavily, you lose some of your body's mineral and water content. Heat illness can result if you fail to drink enough water before, during, and after strenuous activities. Remember that you need to drink one cup of water every 20 minutes when you are exercising to avoid heat-related problems. Everyone should drink at least two quarts of water a day.

THE NEW FOOD LABEL

With the old *food* labels many people had difficulty determining the nutritional value of certain foods and were unable to compare the contents of two food products. The old labels were difficult to understand and inconsistent from one product to another. In an attempt to correct this problem and help consumers make the best nutritional decisions, the federal government has required producers to place a standardized food label on all food products.

The new food label makes it easier for consumers to make comparisons and quickly determine the specific nutritional value of each product. The label looks the same on all food products, contains the same information, and provides that information in a standardized form. The new food label includes a number of new requirements that were not always included on the previous food labels. The chart, Nutrition Facts, identifies features of the new food label.

1. SERVING SIZE
SERVING SIZE AND NUMBER OF SERVINGS IN THE CONTAINER IS GIVEN IN EASILY UNDERSTOOD MEASURES. THIS MAKES IT EASIER TO COMPARE SIMILAR PRODUCTS AND KNOW THE SERVING SIZES ARE BASICALLY IDENTICAL.

2. CALORIES AND FAT
THE TOTAL NUMBER OF CALORIES PER SERVING AND THE AMOUNT OF FAT PER SERVING IS PROVIDED.

3. PERCENT DAILY VALUES
THE PERCENT DAILY VALUES FOR KEY INGREDIENTS IS BASED ON A STANDARDIZED DAILY DIET OF 2000 CALORIES. THIS SECTION OF THE LABEL HELPS THE CONSUMER DETERMINE THE FOODS THAT ARE HIGH OR LOW IN THE REQUIRED DAILY NUTRIENTS.

4. VITAMINS AND MINERALS
PROVIDES INFORMATION ABOUT FOUR IMPORTANT VITAMINS AND MINERALS: VITAMIN A, VITAMIN C, CALCIUM, AND IRON.

5. SUGGESTED DAILY VALUE
THE BOTTOM PORTION OF THE PANEL PRESENTS THE DAILY VALUE THAT SHOULD BE CONSUMED. FIGURES FOR A 2000 AND 2500 DIET ARE PROVIDED FOR COMPARISON.

6. HEALTH BENEFITS
THE NUMBER OF CALORIES CONTAINED IN A SINGLE GRAM OF FAT, CARBOHYDRATE, AND PROTEIN ARE PROVIDED. THIS HELPS THE CONSUMER DETERMINE IF FOOD HAS POTENTIAL FOR LOWERING CANCER RISK.

Nutrition Facts
Serving Size ½ cup (58g)
Servings Per Container about 8

Amount Per Serving

Calories 200

Calories from Fat 10

	% Daily Value*
Total Fat 1g	2%
Saturated Fat 0g	0%
Cholesterol 0mg	0%
Sodium 350mg	15%
Potassium 160mg	5%
Total Carbohydrate 47g	16%
Dietary Fiber 5g	21%
Sugars 7g	
Other Carbohydrate 35g	
Protein 6g	

Vitamin A 25%	•	Vitamin C 0%
Calcium 2%	•	Iron 45%
Vitamin D 10%	•	Thiamin 25%
Riboflavin		25%
Niacin 25%	•	Vitamin B6 25%
Folate		25%
Vitamin B12		25%
Phosphorus		15%
Magnesium		15%
Zinc 8%	•	Copper 10%

*Percent Daily Values are based on a 2,000 calorie diet. Your daily values may be higher or lower depending on your calorie needs:

		Calories: 2,000	2,500
Total Fat	Less than	65g	80g
Sat Fat	Less than	20g	25g
Cholest	Less than	300mg	300mg
Sodium	Less than	2,400mg	2,400mg
Potassium		3,500mg	3,500mg
Total Carbohydrate		300g	375g
Dietary Fiber		25g	30g

INGREDIENTS: WHEAT, MALTED BARLEY, SALT, YEAST.
VITAMINS AND MINERALS: REDUCED IRON, NIACINAMIDE, VITAMIN A PALMITATE, ZINC OXIDE (SOURCE OF ZINC), VITAMIN B6, RIBOFLAVIN (VITAMIN B2), THIAMIN MONONITRATE (VITAMIN B1), VITAMIN B12, FOLIC ACID, VITAMIN D.

1g Fat = 9 calories
1g Carbohydrate = 4 calories
1g Protein = 4 calories

HEALTH CLAIMS AND LEGAL DEFINITIONS

The new food label also provides information on those topics, such as nutrients, that reflect current health concerns. The federal government has approved the following health claims regarding the prevention of cancer.

a. A low fat diet may reduce your risk for cancer.

b. High fiber foods may reduce your risk for cancer.

c. Fruits and vegetables may reduce your risk for cancer.

The regulations prohibit using these claims for one nutrient if the food also contains other nutrients that undermine its benefits. While it is true that a jelly doughnut is high in fiber, it is also high in fat. Therefore, it cannot be claimed that a jelly doughnut should be part of a healthy diet.

Prior to the new labeling law, producers could use the terms "low," "high," and "free," but their meaning could vary from one product to another. Now these terms must meet legal definitions. If a food is described as:

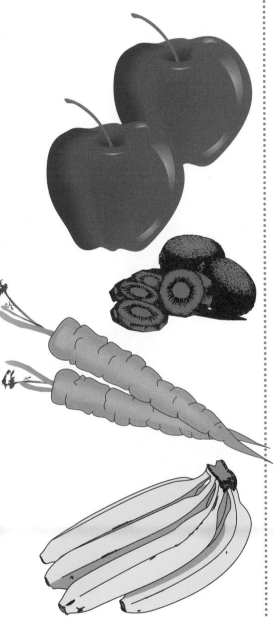

- "high" in a particular nutrient, it must contain 20 percent or more of the daily value for that nutrient.
- "reduced, less, fewer," it must contain 25 percent less of a nutrient or calories than the regular food items.
- "fat free," it must contain only a tiny or insignificant amount of fat, less than 0.5 grams (1/8 of a teaspoon) per serving.
- "low fat," it must contain no more than 3 grams (3/4 of a teaspoon) per serving.
- "lean," it must contain less than 10 grams (2 and 1/2 teaspoons) of fat per serving and less than 4 grams (one teaspoon) of saturated fat and 95 mg of cholesterol per serving.
- "extra lean," it must contain less than 5 grams (1 and 1/4 teaspoon) of fat, 2 grams of saturated fat (1/2 teaspoon), and 95 mg of cholesterol per serving.
- "light/lite," it must contain one-third fewer calories or half the fat of the original.
- "sugar free," it must contain less than 0.5 grams per serving.
- "cholesterol free," it must contain less than 2 mg of cholesterol and 2 grams or less of saturated fat per serving.
- "low cholesterol," it must contain 20 mg or less and 2 grams or less of saturated fat per serving.

CALCULATION OF FAT, CARBOHYDRATE, AND PROTEIN CALORIES

The average daily fat consumption in the American diet is about 37 percent of the total caloric intake, which greatly increases the risk for chronic diseases such as cardiovascular disease, cancer, di-

abetes, and obesity. Less than 30 percent of total calories should come from fat. Of the energy nutrients, carbohydrates and protein both supply the body with four calories per gram, while fat provides nine calories per gram.

One way to monitor the amount of fat in your diet is to look on the food label to see how many fat grams are in a serving. As stated above, each gram of fat equals nine calories. Multiply the grams of fat by 9 and divide by the total number of calories in a serving. Multiply this number by 100 to determine the percent of calories from fat. For example, if a food label lists a total of 150 calories and 13 grams of fat, the fat content is 78 percent of the total calories. It is recommended that only 30 percent of your total daily caloric intake come from fat.

Calculation of Percent Fat Calories

Formula:
Percent of Fat Calories = (grams of fat × 9)/calories per serving × 100

Example:
One beef hot dog has:
        13 grams of fat per serving
        150 total calories per serving
Therefore:
        13 grams × 9 calories per gram = 117 calories
        117/150 × 100 = 78% fat*

*This means that 78 percent of the calories from one beef hot dog are obtained from fat.

You could also figure the percent of protein and carbohydrate calories provided by a certain food by using this same formula. By reading the label you can determine the total grams of fat, protein, or carbohydrate and substitute in the formula accordingly. Since fat provides more than twice the number of calories per gram (9) than either carbohydrates (4) or protein (4), it is recommended that you eat more carbohydrates. By using this simple formula, you will have useful information on which to base your food selections and decrease the amount of fat in your diet.

THE FOOD GUIDE PYRAMID

The **Food Guide Pyramid** is a simple guideline to help you select foods for proper nutrition. Proper nutrition means that an individual's diet supplies all of the essential nutrients necessary to carry out the body's normal processes of growth, repair, and maintenance.

The amounts of carbohydrates, fats, and proteins contained in our diet are measured in calories. A calorie is the unit of measure for the potential energy that the body can obtain from a certain amount of food. A chemical reaction must take place for a calorie of carbohydrate, fat, or protein to actually become energy.

The Food Guide Pyramid was developed by the United States Department of Agriculture in recognition of the value that all foods have in an individual's daily diet plan. Foods are categorized into six food groups according to the nutrients they contain. Since some nutrients are needed in greater amounts than others, the number of servings from each food group varies. The six food groups and the recommended number of servings are shown below.

FOOD GUIDE PYRAMID

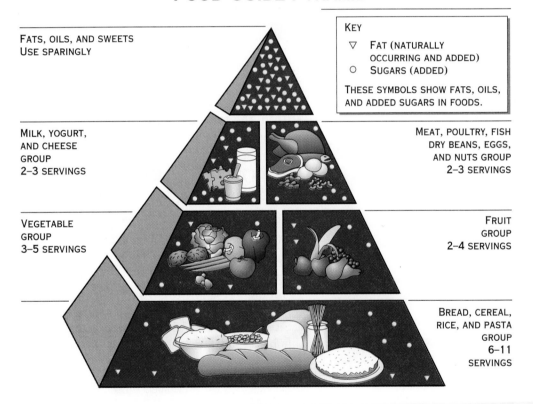

FATS, OILS, AND SWEETS
USE SPARINGLY

KEY
▽ FAT (NATURALLY OCCURRING AND ADDED)
○ SUGARS (ADDED)
THESE SYMBOLS SHOW FATS, OILS, AND ADDED SUGARS IN FOODS.

MILK, YOGURT, AND CHEESE GROUP
2–3 SERVINGS

MEAT, POULTRY, FISH DRY BEANS, EGGS, AND NUTS GROUP
2–3 SERVINGS

VEGETABLE GROUP
3–5 SERVINGS

FRUIT GROUP
2–4 SERVINGS

BREAD, CEREAL, RICE, AND PASTA GROUP
6–11 SERVINGS

Table 9–1 provides sample serving size for each food group. Appendix E gives the size of a serving for a variety of foods in each food group and their caloric content. Table 9–2 provides the number of daily servings for each food group necessary to meet individual needs. The amount you eat at one meal could amount to more than one serving. For example, a dinner portion of spaghetti would count as either two or three servings of pasta.

Along with exercise, eating a variety of foods based on the Food Guide Pyramid has proven to be an effective way to assist individuals in reaching and maintaining their ideal body weight. Individ-

Table 9–1. Sample Serving Size	
Breads, cereals, rice, and pasta 1 slice of bread ½ cup of cooked rice or pasta ½ cup of cooked cereal 1 ounce of ready-to-eat cereal	**Milk, yogurt, and cheese** 1 cup of milk or yogurt 1½ to 2 ounces of cheese
Vegetables ½ cup of chopped, raw, or cooked vegetables 1 cup of leafy raw vegetables egg,	**Meat, poultry, fish, dry beans, eggs, and nuts** 2½ to 3 ounces of cooked lean meat, poultry or fish Count ½ cup of cooked beans, or 1
Fruits 1 piece of fruit or melon wedge ¾ cup of juice ½ cup of canned fruit ¼ cup of dried fruit	or 2 tablespoons of peanut butter as 1 ounce of lean meat (about ⅓ serving) **Fats, oils, and sweets** *Limit calories from these*, especially if you need to lose weight

uals who need to gain weight, lose weight, or are involved in extremely vigorous exercise programs, may need to modify the recommended size of each serving. Athletes may wish to add servings from the food groups that will provide additional calories of carbohydrates.

A CLOSER LOOK AT FAT AND ADDED SUGARS

The small tip of the pyramid shows fats, oils, and sweets. These are foods such as salad dressings, cream, butter, margarine, sugars, soft drinks, candies, and sweet desserts. Alcoholic beverages are also part of this group. These foods are called empty calorie foods because they provide many calories with few nutrients. People should eat very little from this group.

Table 9–2. Number of Servings Daily to Meet Individual Needs			
	Women & some older adults	Children, teenage girls, active women, most men	Teenage boys & active men
Calorie level*	about 1,600	about 2,200	about 2,800
Bread group	6	9	11
Vegetable group	3	4	5
Fruit group	2	3	4
Milk group	**2–3	**2–3	**2–3
Meat group	2, for a total of 5 ounces	2, for a total of 6 ounces	3, for a total of 7 ounces

*These are the calorie levels if you choose low fat, lean foods from the five major food groups and use foods from the fats, oils, and sweets group sparingly.

**Women who are pregnant or breast feeding, teenagers, and young adults to age 24 need 3 servings.

Source: USDA

Some fat or sugar symbols are shown in the other food groups to remind you that some foods in these groups (cheese or ice cream from the milk group and french fries from the vegetable group) can also be high in fat and added sugars. When choosing foods for a healthful diet, consider the fat and added sugars in your choices from all the food groups, not just the fats, oils, and sweets from the group at the pyramid tip.

FOOD GROUPS IN THE FOOD GUIDE PYRAMID

Examples of foods included in each group are listed below.

Bread, Cereal, Rice, and Pasta Group (6–11 servings) Enriched breads and cereals are our major energy source, since they contain large amounts of carbohydrates. This group also furnishes the body with the most fiber and also provides vitamins and minerals. You need to eat more servings per day from this group than from any other.

Bread, Cereal, Rice, and Pasta Group

Vegetable Group (3–5 servings) The vegetable group includes a large variety of foods from plants. Vegetables are a good source of fiber and the major source of vitamins and minerals. One serving of a dark green or deep yellow vegetable should be eaten each day; it will provide vitamin A.

Vegetable Group

Fruit Group

Fruit Group (2–4 servings) Fruits are a good source of fiber and a major source of vitamins and minerals. Citrus fruit provides an excellent source for vitamin C. Since vitamin C is a water soluble vitamin and cannot be stored in the body, one piece of citrus fruit or glass of juice should be consumed daily.

Milk, Yogurt, and Cheese Group (2–3 servings) Foods in this group come mostly from animals and are good sources of protein, calcium, iron, and zinc. When looking at the nutritional value of milk products, it is interesting to note that the only difference between whole milk and a 2-percent product is the fat content. Eating low-fat cheese, sour cream, and ice milk will reduce the amount of fat consumed and the possibility of cardiovascular diseases.

Milk, Yogurt, and Cheese Group

Meat, Poultry, Fish, Dry Beans, Eggs, and Nuts Group (2–3 servings) This food group is the major source of protein and iron essential for the growth and repair of tissue, but it is also a major source of fat. You should select foods from this group that have a lower fat content. For example, fish and poultry have a lower fat content than beef or pork. It is also recommended that you eat small portions. Only six ounces from this group are needed daily.

Meat, Poultry, Fish, Dry Beans, Eggs, and Nuts Group

Fats, Oils, and Sweets Group

Fats, Oils, and Sweets Group (sparingly) Included in this group are condiments such as salad dressing, butter and margarine, and a variety of cooking oils. Most of these should be used sparingly because of the fat and sugar content.

A truly balanced daily diet does not eliminate any of the first five food categories. If you are short of servings from one of the food groups on a regular basis, you may not be getting enough of the nutrients supplied by that group. It is essential that you eat a variety of foods in order to obtain all of the nutrients needed.

Although the basic food groups included in the pyramid contain a variety of possibilities, many individuals fail to take advantage of the variety. The point to remember is that you can eat a balanced diet and still make highly individual food choices.

DETERMINING DAILY CALORIE REQUIREMENTS

The daily calorie requirement for each person is different. How many calories a person requires to support daily body functions depends on two factors: body mass and amount of physical activity. The greater the body mass, the more calories required to support that body mass. The same is true for level of physical activity—the more active you are, the more calories required to support your body. If a construction worker and a secretary have the same body size, the construction worker will require more calories just to maintain and support daily activities.

BASAL METABOLISM

Basal metabolism is the amount of energy required to simply maintain your body at rest. This rate of metabolism is reduced with age. Therefore, caloric intake to support basic metabolism should be reduced with age. Basal metabolism is usually estimated as one calorie per kilogram of body weight per hour. To determine basal metabolism, you must convert your body weight from pounds to kilograms. One kilogram is equal to 2.2 pounds. Suppose that John weighs 140 pounds or 63.64 kilograms (140 divided by 2.2). To determine how many calories he needs to eat just to maintain his body at rest, he has to multiply his body weight in kilograms (63.64) by 24 hours. This amounts to 1,527 calories (63.64 × 24) needed to maintain the basic functioning of his body, without considering his daily physical activity.

Your body burns calories even when you are sleeping. The amount of energy needed to maintain your body while you are sleeping is called basal metabolism.

To Determine Basal Metabolism Requirements:

Step 1 Convert body weight to kilograms.
140 (body weight)/2.2 = 63.64 kg.

Step 2 Multiply kilograms of body weight by 24 hours.
63.64 (kg.) × 24 (hrs.) = 1,527 calories

CALORIC NEEDS FOR DAILY ACTIVITIES

To determine the calories required to support his daily activities in addition to his basal metabolism, or his non-sleeping activities, John should use Table 9–3 and Table 10–1. The figures in those two tables represent the number of calories above basal metabolism required to perform certain types of daily activities. To estimate the number of calories required to support daily activities in addition to basal metabolism, estimate the number of hours you spend performing different types of activities included in Table 9–3 and Table 10–1. Multiply the number of hours for each type of activity times the number of calories required per hour, and

Table 9–3. Energy Expenditures for Various Activities			
Daily Activities	Calories Per 1/2 Hour	Daily Activities	Calories Per 1/2 Hour
Cooking	40	Making beds	60
Dressing	40	Marketing	40
Driving car	25	Mowing lawn (hand mower)	93
Dusting	40	Office work	38
Eating	15	Sawing or chopping wood	150
Gardening	68	Sitting or doing quiet seated work	15
Ironing (standing)	23	Standing	20
		Washing floor	65

then add the total number of calories for all activities. This method is further explained in Chapter 10.

DAILY DIET

Your daily diet should be based on the Food Guide Pyramid. If your daily activities include a lot of physical activities, such as athletics, you may want to add one or two servings of bread, cereal, rice, or pasta all of which are high in carbohydrates. If you are very active, you may also want to add one or two servings from the fruit and the vegetable food groups. It is important to remember that when you are no longer in sports competition, you should reduce your servings to meet the normal guidelines for your age group, since you will no longer need the extra calories.

A complete diet diary can help you evaluate your diet to see if you have a balanced diet and to determine if you are eating too many or too few calories.

KEEP A DIET LOG

The first step in evaluating your diet is to keep a daily diet log; that is, write down everything you eat. The best method is to keep the diet log for one week, since your lifestyle is likely to be similar from week to week. If you keep a diet log for only a few days, it may indicate a higher or lower caloric intake than you really have over a long period of time. For example, if you kept a diet log for only three or four days during the week but did not include the weekend, your caloric intake would be low because the pizza you had with friends over the weekend would not have been included.

Once you have completed the diet log, you are ready to evaluate your eating patterns. First, look to see if you included the first five

Sound nutrition contributes to a happy, active lifestyle.

food groups of the Food Guide Pyramid and if you ate the suggested number of servings from each group. You should not be too critical of yourself if you did not meet the recommended daily servings for a specific day. However, you should average the recommendations over the period of a few days. Next, estimate the number of calories you ate each day. Use Appendix E to determine the caloric content of the foods included in your diet. Now compare your estimated daily output and your estimated daily intake. If your intake is greater, check to see where you could have cut extra calories. If your output was greater, check to see if you had enough servings from the bread and cereal group or if you were short on servings from the milk group. How to adjust your diet, whether you want to gain weight or lose weight and still maintain good nutrition, will be discussed in Chapter 10.

GOOD NUTRITION HELPS YOU LOOK GOOD AND FEEL GOOD

Eating a diet that contains the required number of servings recommended by the Food Guide Pyramid with a sufficient number of calories to maintain a desired weight will go a long way toward giving you the figure or body build, complexion, or glossy hair that will make you look good and feel good.

SUMMARY

You are what you eat. This may be a cliche, but it is true. Teenagers and adults who look good and feel good and who lead an active lifestyle eat a sound nutritional diet. The nutritional habits of most people are developed from family, ethnic background, and lifestyle. Many of these habits may not be the best for you. The effects of poor eating habits are not immediately visible. Just as consuming extra calories will lead to creeping obesity, poor nutrition over a period of time will lead to health problems.

Your body requires the essential nutrients to function properly and stay healthy. These nutrients include proteins, carbohydrates, fats, minerals, and vitamins. However, there are also some health concerns related to these essential nutrients, like cholesterol and essential amino acids, so it is not just the amount you eat from each of the six food groups in the Food Guide Pyramid.

TRUE-FALSE

Circle "T" for all correct statements and "F" for all incorrect ones.

T F 1. Eating habits are closely related to such health problems as complexion, overweight, and high cholesterol levels.

T F 2. Proteins are a better source of energy than carbohydrates.

T F 3. Cholesterol is contained in saturated fats.

T F 4. The good type of cholesterol that is stored on the artery walls is LDL, which stands for the least desirable lipoprotein.

T F 5. Minerals are often lost during food preparation because a chemical reaction occurs when certain foods are mixed.

T F 6. Vitamins are used by the body to aid in the use of other nutrients.

T F 7. A person should drink at least two quarts of water each day.

T F 8. The Food Guide Pyramid is a guideline to help insure that energy needs during exercise will be met by our diet.

T F 9. The food group highest in fiber is the meat and poultry group.

T F 10. If you want to gain weight or if you are very active, you may want to increase the number of servings in the bread and cereal group.

DISCUSSION

11. What are the health problems that are directly related to nutritional habits?
12. Describe how you would use a diet dairy to evaluate your diet?
13. Plan a balanced diet for one day using the Food Guide Pyramid?
14. Why are minerals and vitamins considered essential nutrients?
15. Calculate the daily caloric requirements for an active teenager.

BODY COMPOSITION AND WEIGHT CONTROL

10

CHAPTER OBJECTIVES

As you read this chapter, look for answers to these key questions:

- What are the characteristics of the three classifications of body types?

- How do you determine how much of your body weight is fat and how much is lean body mass?

- What medical problems are associated with excessive body fat?

- Why are fat children and fat teenagers likely to become fat adults?

- What is the difference between being overweight and obese?

- What three methods can a person use to lose weight?

- Why is permanent weight control best achieved by a combination of diet and exercise?

RX FOR LOOKING GOOD AND FEELING GOOD

Everyone wants to be as attractive and healthy as possible. Today people are becoming more concerned about their physical appearance. There is a greater awareness of diet and exercise than ever before. This can be seen by the growth in businesses such as weight reduction centers, aerobic dance studios, health clubs, and in an endless number of fitness and weight-control products.

The goal for many is to appear as healthy and as attractive as possible. Looking good and feeling good about yourself are important personal goals.

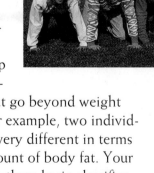

BODY TYPES

It is important for you to know why you appear as you do. People have different body types because of the specific genetic makeup they inherited from their parents and grandparents. Body types describe differences that go beyond weight and height measurements in individuals. For example, two individuals of identical weight and height may be very different in terms of bone structure, muscle structure, and amount of body fat. Your body type is called a **somatotype**. There are three basic classifications of somatotype: endomorph, mesomorph, and ectomorph.

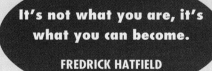

153

ENDOMORPH

A large, soft, bulging body and a pear-shaped appearance characterize a pure **endomorph**. Features of this body type are shown in the drawing.

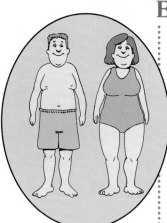

- high percentage of body fat
- short neck
- large abdomen
- wide hips
- round, full buttocks
- short, heavy legs

MESOMORPH

A solid, muscular, and large-boned physique characterize a pure **mesomorph**. Features of this body type are shown in the drawing.

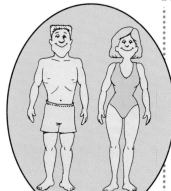

- firm, well developed muscles
- large bones
- broad shoulders
- muscular arms
- trim waist
- muscular buttocks
- powerful legs

ECTOMORPH

A slender body and slight build characterize a pure **ecto-morph**. Features of this body type are shown in the drawing.

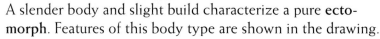

- small bones
- thin muscles
- slender arms and legs
- narrow chest
- round shoulders
- flat abdomen
- small buttocks

Very few people are either pure endomorphs, mesomorphs, or ectomorphs. Some people have characteristics of all three body types. Most people are a combination of two types.

You inherit your body type from your parents and grandparents. This means you are born with a tendency toward a certain basic body type. Gaining weight is harder for individuals with ectomorphic characteristics. Staying lean is more difficult for individuals with endomorphic characteristics. Even though heredity influences what your body looks like, what you eat and how much you exercise can play important roles in determing your overall appearance.

How much you weigh is not as important as your actual body composition.

BODY COMPOSITION

You can easily see how much you weigh by getting on a scale. But what does your weight consist of? Is it mostly muscle? Is it fat? Is it bone? Your body weight is a combination of all three. Together, muscle, bone, and fat make up what is called **body composition**. Recall that body composition is one of the health-related components of physical fitness, along with flexibility, cardiovascular fitness, muscular strength, and muscular endurance.

LEAN BODY MASS VERSUS BODY FAT

Lean body mass is muscle tissue and other nonfat tissue such as bones, ligaments, and tendons. Body fat results from stored calories that have not been burned up. The distribution of your lean body mass and body fat can change depending upon how active you are, how much you eat, and how fast you are growing.

Determining your body composition involves measuring your percentage of body fat as precisely as possible. By knowing the percentage of body fat, you can determine the percentage of lean body mass. For example, if a person weighs 140 pounds and has 20 percent body fat, then 28 pounds of the weight is fat (140 lbs. × 20% = 28 lbs.). The other 80 percent, or 112 pounds, is lean body mass.

HEIGHT AND WEIGHT CHARTS CAN BE MISLEADING

People review standard height and weight charts to see how much they should weigh. The ranges on height and weight charts represent average weights and can be misleading. They do not tell you how much of your weight is lean body mass and how much is body fat. For example, a person who does not exercise regularly could be in the acceptable range according to a height and weight chart, but have excessive fat. On the other hand, a muscular person might be considered overweight according to a height and weight chart, yet have very little body fat. A point to remember is that muscle mass weighs more and takes up less space than the same amount of fat tissue.

Many people have the mistaken belief that their body weight is crucial. How much you weigh is not as important as your actual body composition. Weighing yourself cannot be used to determine your percentage of body fat and lean body mass. Therefore, it is important to periodically measure your body fat and make sure that most of the weight you are gaining is lean body mass.

**ACCORDING TO HEIGHT
AND WEIGHT CHARTS:**

OVERWEIGHT VERSUS OBESE

Overweight and obese are words often used interchangeably. However, they do not mean the same. In order to obtain your proper or ideal body weight, it is important to understand the meanings of these terms.

Overweight people are those who exceed their desirable body weight by 10 percent, according to height and weight charts. Remember, height and weight charts do not tell you how much of your body weight is fat. You can be overweight on height and weight charts and still have an acceptable level of body fat. Remember that muscle weighs more than body fat and takes up less space.

Obese people are those who have an excessive amount of body fat. You can be obese without being overweight. It is not how heavy you are but rather how much excess body fat you have that is important to your health and appearance.

IDEAL BODY WEIGHT

Ideal body weight is the amount you would weigh if you have an appropriate percentage of body fat. It has also been described as the weight at which you look good and feel the most comfortable. It is the healthiest weight for your body.

The proper or ideal percentage of body fat varies with age and sex. The chart below illustrates acceptable ranges of body fat. A person should try to stay below the upper limits given in the chart. A person at the lower limit would be described as lean.

Age	Males	Females
up to 30	9%–15%	14%–21%
30–50	11%–17%	15%–23%
50 and up	12%–19%	16%–25%

As you can see, the ideal weight for your body is an individual and personal matter. There is no single ideal body weight for people with the same body size and shape. For example, an athlete may weigh more than others of his age and height, but the extra weight is in the form of muscle, not fat. On the other hand, a person who does very little exercise may weigh as much as the athlete but have too much body fat.

METHODS OF MEASURING BODY FAT

Methods most commonly used for measuring body fat are underwater weighing, skinfold measurements, and measurements of body circumference. Underwater weighing is the most accurate means for measuring body fat. However, it requires specialized, costly equipment and highly trained individuals to operate the equipment.

UNDERWATER WEIGHING

Underwater weighing is the most accurate means for testing body fat. This method requires a large water tank or swimming pool and a weighing scale. First the person is weighed in air on a scale and then weighed underwater.

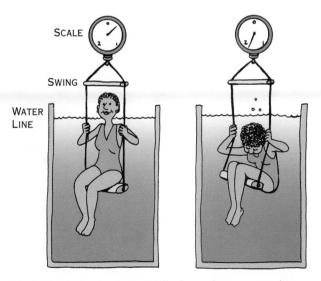

The individual submerges totally for underwater weighing.

SKINFOLD MEASUREMENTS

Another method for assessing body fat is to measure skinfold. This technique utilizes an instrument called a **skinfold caliper** to measure a fold of skin and its underlying layer of fat at key locations on the body. Approximately half of your body fat is located deep within your body. The other half is found underneath your skin between the skin and muscles. The diagram below shows how a skinfold caliper measures the thickness of a fold of skin and its underlying layer of fat. Special computations provide your percentage of body fat based on the various measurements of skinfold thickness.

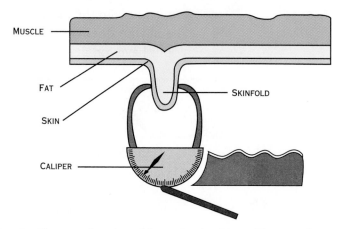

Drawing illustrates location of fat under the skin and how a caliper is used to measure the thickness of a skinfold.

BODY CIRCUMFERENCE MEASUREMENTS

The least accurate method for determining percentage of body fat is the measurement of body circumference. This method uses the circumference of selected body parts plus your weight. A cloth measuring tape and a scale are the only equipment needed for this method. Special computations provide your percentage of body fat.

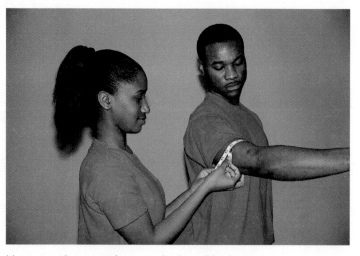

Measuring the circumference of selected body parts

Weight control is a major health problem in the United States. It is estimated that more than half the adults in this country are overweight. Research has found American youth to be fatter than they have been at any time in the past thirty years. It is believed that this is due to a higher standard of living, increased mechanization, more leisure time, less physical activity, insufficient knowledge about weight control, and a lack of motivation in regard to weight control.

EXCESS FAT IS UNHEALTHY

Although some body fat is necessary, it is now an accepted medical fact that excess fat is bad for your health. Research shows that American men who are obese have a life expectancy that is 20 percent shorter than men of average weight. Obese women have a life expectancy that is 10 percent shorter than women of average weight. People with excessive fat have a greater likelihood of developing medical problems. Health hazards from excessive fat include:

-breathing difficulties
-kidney disorders
-diabetes
-surgical risk
-cancer
-pregnancy problems
-high blood pressure
-less resistance to infections
-heart disease
-shortened life expectancy
-stroke
-social discrimination

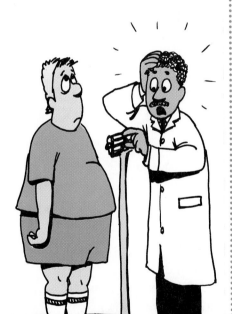

Weight control is a major health problem.

Excess body fat is not only unhealthy, it also keeps you from looking, feeling, and performing as well as you can. Feeling good about your weight and understanding how to obtain and maintain your proper or ideal body weight are important goals in personal fitness.

VULNERABLE STAGES FOR FAT CELL GROWTH

There are three major time periods in your life when fat cells are primarily formed: (1) during the last month of fetal development, (2) during the first year of life, and (3) during the growth spurt of adolescence. Your total number of fat cells becomes permanently established once you reach adulthood.

LIMIT FAT CELLS NOW

When adolescents and children grow fatter, an increase in the size of existing fat cells and an increase in the number of fat cells occur. When adults grow fatter, only an increase in the size of existing fat cells occurs.

Fat children and fat teenagers are more likely to become fat adults because they have developed more fat cells. These extra fat cells make it easier to get fatter. Weight control is more difficult for individuals who have extra fat cells. However, with adequate exercise and proper diet, people with extra fat cells can achieve and maintain their ideal body weight.

CREEPING OBESITY

As people reach adulthood, they usually start to gain weight. Excess calories add up day by day, month by month, and year by year. People do not become overweight or obese overnight, but over a period of time. The slow gaining of fat over a period of years is called **creeping obesity**.

An excess of ten calories per day beyond what you need over a year results in one additional pound of fat. After ten years you will have gained ten pounds and will begin to experience what is referred to as middle-age spread. Maybe you have noticed this occurring in your parents or their friends. If there is an excess of 100 calories (one slice of bread) per day for one year, the weight gain is ten pounds. This translates to one dress size larger for women. Over a five-year period, the dress size creeps from a size 6 to a size 14.

Middle-age spread

The average weight gain for Americans between the ages of 25 and 55 is 30 pounds. Since an increase in age is usually accompanied by a decrease in the basal metabolic rate and a decrease in physical activity, the weight gained is more likely to be fat tissue than muscle tissue.

Creeping obesity does not have to happen. You can maintain your ideal body weight throughout your life by exercising regularly and eating a proper diet.

WEIGHT LOSS, WEIGHT GAIN, AND WEIGHT MAINTENANCE

Recall that a calorie is a measure of energy the body is able to produce from food. Each pound of weight is equivalent to approximately 3,500 calories. To gain a pound, you must take in and store

3,500 calories. To lose a pound, you must burn off that number of calories.

To reach your ideal body weight, you must balance what you eat (caloric intake) against what your body uses (caloric output). Weight loss or weight gain can be achieved by (1) changing caloric intake, (2) changing caloric output, or (3) a combination of the two.

WEIGHT LOSS

You must unbalance your caloric intake or output to have a weight loss. To lose a pound a week (1 pound = 3,500 calories), you could do one of the following:

1. Eat 500 calories less each day than your average daily caloric output.

2. Add exercise each day in an amount that would be equal to burning 500 calories.

3. Do a combination of 1 and 2, such as eating 250 calories less and engaging in exercise that would be equal to burning 250 calories.

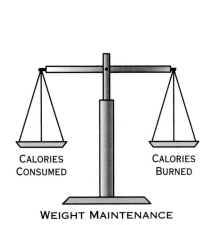

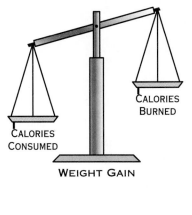

To have a weight loss or weight gain you must unbalance your caloric intake or output. To maintain weight you must balance your caloric intake and output.

WEIGHT GAIN

You must also unbalance your caloric intake or output to gain weight. To gain a pound a week (1 pound = 3,500 calories), you could do one of the following:

1. Eat 500 calories more each day than your average daily caloric output.

2. Reduce your exercise each day by an amount that would be equal to burning 500 calories.

3. Do a combination of 1 and 2, such as eating 250 calories more and reducing your exercise by an amount that would be equal to burning 250 calories.

WEIGHT MAINTENANCE

To maintain weight, your average daily caloric intake should be the same as your average daily caloric output. In other words, you have to consume as many calories as your body burns.

CALORIC COST OF PHYSICAL ACTIVITIES

Number of calories burned depends on a number of factors.

You use up calories when you exercise. How many calories you use during any activity depends upon the intensity at which you perform the activity, the length of time you perform it, your skill level, and your body weight. The approximate caloric cost of various activities is shown in the Estimated Caloric Cost of Selected Activities chart.

To calculate the caloric cost for a given activity, take the number of calories burned per minute per pound and multiply it by your weight and the number of minutes the activity is performed. For example, a 120-pound individual running at a rate of six miles per hour (10 minutes/mile) would burn 284 calories during a 30-minute period.

0.079 calories/minute/pound	×	120 weight	×	30 minutes	=	284 calories

The best kinds of activities for losing weight are those that burn the most calories per minute. Such activities include bicycling, running, swimming, basketball, soccer, handball, racquetball, and cross country skiing.

10-3

The first numbers column provides an estimate of the number of calories burned per minute per pound of body weight for selected activities. The three weight classification examples provide an estimate of the number of calories burned in the various activities during a 30-minute period.

Your weight has an effect on the number of calories burned.

Table 10–1. Estimated Caloric Cost of Selected Activities

The first column of numbers provides an estimate of the calories burned per minute per pound of body weight for selected activities. The three weight classification examples provide an estimate of the number of calories burned in the various activities during a 30-minute period.

Activity	Cal/min/lb	100 lb	140 lb	180 lb
Archery	.034	102	143	184
Badminton:				
moderate	.039	117	164	211
vigorous	.065	195	273	351
Baseball:				
infield/outfield	.031	93	130	167
pitching	.039	117	164	211
Basketball:				
moderate	.047	141	197	254
vigorous	.066	198	277	356
Bicycling:				
slow (5 mph)	.025	75	105	135
moderate (10 mph)	.05	150	210	270
fast (13 mph)	.072	216	302	389
Bowling	.028	84	118	151
Calisthenics	.045	135	189	243
Canoeing:				
2.5 mph	.023	69	97	124
4.0 mph	.047	141	197	254
Dancing:				
slow	.029	87	122	157
moderate	.045	135	189	243
fast	.064	192	269	346
Fencing:				
moderate	.033	99	139	178
vigorous	.057	171	239	308
Fishing	.016	48	67	86
Football (tag)	.04	120	168	216
Golf	.029	87	122	157
Gymnastics:				
light	.022	66	92	119
heavy	.056	168	235	302
Handball	.063	189	265	340
Hiking	.042	126	176	227
Hill Climbing	.06	180	252	324
Horseback Riding:				
walk	.019	57	80	103
trot	.046	138	193	248
gallop	.067	201	281	362

Table 10–1. *continued*			
Activity	Cal/min/lb	100 lb	140 lb	180 lb
---	---	---	---	---
Jogging: 4.5 mph (13:30 min/mi)	.063	189	265	340
Judo	.087	261	365	470
Karate	.087	261	365	470
Mountain Climbing	.086	258	361	464
Racquetball	.069	207	290	373
Rowing: moderate (2.5 mph) vigorous	.036 .118	108 354	151 496	194 637
Running: 6 mph (10 min/mi) 10 mph (6 min/mi)	.079 .1	237 300	332 420	427 540
Sailing	.02	60	84	180
Skating: moderate vigorous	.036 .064	108 192	151 269	194 346
Skiing (snow): downhill cross country	.059 .078	177 234	248 328	319 421
Soccer	.063	189	265	340
Squash	.07	210	294	378
Stationary Running: 70–80 counts/min	.078	234	328	421
Swimming (crawl) 20 yards/min. 45 yards/min. 50 yards/min.	.032 .058 .071	96 174 213	134 244 298	173 313 383
Table Tennis: moderate vigorous	.026 .04	78 120	109 168	140 216
Tennis: moderate vigorous	.046 .06	138 180	193 252	248 324
Volleyball: moderate vigorous	.036 .065	108 195	151 273	194 351
Walking: slow moderate fast	.023 .032 .044	69 96 132	97 134 185	124 173 208
Water Skiing	.053	159	223	286
Weight Training	.05	150	210	270
Wrestling	.091	273	382	491

10-4

Achieving and maintaining your ideal body weight can be realized through three methods: (1) diet, (2) exercise, or (3) a combination of diet and exercise. The combination of proper diet and exercise is the best way to achieve and maintain your ideal body weight. One advantage of the combined method is that neither food reduction nor the increase in exercise needs to be as severe as when either is practiced alone. Another advantage is that weight loss is mostly fat, not lean tissue. However, this is not true when you attempt a weight-reduction program by dieting without exercise. When you lose weight by this method, lean tissue is lost along with fat. Dieting alone also slows down your metabolism, which makes fat loss more difficult and can cause fatigue. Exercise speeds up metabolism, burns calories, and decreases body fat. Another important advantage of combining diet and exercise is the improvement of flexibility, cardiovascular fitness, muscular strength, and muscular endurance.

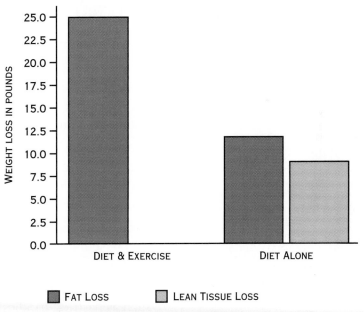

A combination of dieting and exercise will cause more fat to be lost. Dieting alone will result in a loss of lean tissue, as well as fat.

EATING SMART

Eating smart is important to achieving and maintaining your ideal body weight. Smart eating habits help you look good and feel good, have plenty of energy for schoolwork and leisure activities, and keep your body healthy now and in the future.

Eating smart is not difficult. It simply means being knowledgeable about the amounts and kinds of food you eat. The following recommendations will help you eat smart.

1. Increase your consumption of fruits, vegetables, pastas, breads, unsweetened cereals, and grains such as barley, wheat, oats, cornmeal, and rice.

2. Reduce your consumption of red meats such as beef, pork, and lamb.

3. Increase your consumption of chicken, turkey, and fish.

INSTEAD OF...	TRY...
FRIED CHICKEN BREAST WITH SKIN	BAKED CHICKEN BREAST WITHOUT SKIN
FRENCH FRIES (6 OZ)	BAKED POTATO WITH MARGARINE (1 PAT)
COLE SLAW (3 OZ)	COOKED CARROTS (3 OZ)
WHOLE MILK (1 CUP)	SKIM MILK (1 CUP)
VANILLA ICE CREAM (4 OZ)	VANILLA NON-FAT FROZEN YOGURT (4 OZ)
TOTAL	TOTAL
CALORIES: 1079	CALORIES: 760
FAT: 49 GM*	FAT: 10 GM*
SATURATED FAT: 20 GM	SATURATED FAT: 2 GM
CHOLESTROL: 241 MG	CHOLESTEROL: 150 MG
*41% CALORIES FROM FAT	*12% CALORIES FROM FAT

Eat smart! Build a better meal.

4. Eat foods that are broiled or baked rather than fried. Frying doubles the number of calories in foods. A broiled chicken leg has 45 calories and a fried chicken leg has 90.

5. Reduce your consumption of high-fat foods such as eggs, butter, whole milk, ice cream, all fried foods, and whole-milk cheeses.

6. Reduce your consumption of high-cholesterol foods such as bacon, sour cream, hot dogs, hamburgers, luncheon meats, and gravies.

7. Reduce your consumption of foods containing a lot of sugar such as pastries, candies, sweetened drinks, honey, jams, jellies, syrups, most desserts, and sweetened cereals.

8. Reduce your consumption of table salt and foods high in salt such as potato chips, crackers, condiments, pickles, and canned fish.

Following these guidelines does not mean that you should never eat a hamburger or French fries. These recommendations should be used as a guide to help you become more aware of what foods you eat.

Eating smart means looking at your diet as a giant balance sheet. When you eat foods that may not be nutritionally good for you, balance your diet with foods that are nutritionally better. For example, if you eat bacon and eggs for breakfast, eat a fruit salad for lunch.

LONG-HAUL CONCEPT

Weight loss is usually permanent if it is done gradually. It is recommended that you lose no more than one to two pounds per week. This is called the long-haul approach to weight reduction.

Being overweight is not the real problem. Bad habits that lead to being overweight are the problem. It is important that you develop proper eating and exercise habits, which will help ensure that you keep the weight off once your ideal body weight is reached. Your goal should be to get it off and keep it off, using the long-haul concept. Or better still, never put on the extra weight. Most people look their best and feel their best both physically and mentally when they maintain their ideal body weight.

The following behavioral modifications can be beneficial when you are trying to lose or maintain your weight:

1. Keep a record of what, when, and where you eat. Look for a pattern of bad habits, such as eating candy when you are upset. You are more likely to be successful if you try to modify one bad habit rather than tackling two or three at a time.

2. Avoid eating while reading or watching television. A whole bag of potato chips can be consumed before you know it.

3. When eating snacks, do not eat out of the bag. Rather, pour out a small amount into a bowl. Remember: ten potato chips are equal to 100 calories.

4. Eat breakfast every day. Those who skip this meal usually snack before lunch, eating less nutritious food and more calories than if they had eaten breakfast.

5. Drink a glass of water before you sit down for a meal. The water will help your stomach feel fuller.

6. Eat slowly by chewing your food well. If you eat small portions and are still hungry, wait twenty minutes. It takes this long for the stomach to transmit a signal to the brain that it is full.

Some habits, such as chewing your foods slowly, will help you lose weight.

GOAL SETTING FOR BODY COMPOSITION

Body composition is a health-related physical fitness component that must be improved slowly over a long period of time. Short-term goals for individuals whose skinfold measurements are initially within the category of substantially "less" than the standard should be established carefully and revised as success is achieved. Remember that changes in body composition should be accomplished by changing eating and exercise habits, not by going on drastic diets. If your skinfold measures are 10 mm or more below the health fitness standard, you should set six-month improvement goals to improve from 2 to 15 mm. If your test score falls in the category of "close" to the standard, you should set goals with a range of improvement from 1 to 10 mm. If you "exceed" the health fitness standard, you should set you goal to improve from 1 to 3 mm. Improvement here should be interpreted to mean either gain or lose.

Body Composition			
	Distance from Health Fitness Standard		
	Less	Close	Exceeds
Difference Between Test Score and Health Fitness Standard	More than 10 mm	1 to 10 mm	0 or better
Recommended Range for Goals	1 to 15 mm	1 to 10 mm	1 to 3 mm +/−

EATING DISORDERS

Unfortunately some people become so obsessed with the fear of being overweight that they refuse to eat normally. This disorder is called **anorexia nervosa**. Anorexics have distorted body images. They often look like walking skeletons. People suffering from anorexia nervosa can starve to death or die from severe vitamin and mineral deficiencies.

Another eating disorder is **bulimia**. Bulimics use laxatives and self-induced vomiting to avoid gaining weight. They frequently eat too much food, then get rid of it by inducing vomiting, using laxatives, and exercising very strenuously. These repeated actions can cause serious medical problems.

Anorexia nervosa and bulimia are very serious eating disorders. People suffering from these disorders need both medical and psychological advice. If you know someone who has one of these disorders, encourage them to seek help.

WEIGHT CONTROL MISCONCEPTIONS

Because of the emphasis placed on weight control in our society, some misconceptions have developed about exercise and weight control. The following misconceptions are most common.

EXERCISE AND FAT LOSS

Some people believe that participating in physical activity will not help them lose weight because of the time it takes to burn 3,500 calories through exercise. This myth comes from those who say it takes eight and a half hours of playing tennis, eleven and a half hours of walking, or seven hours of splitting wood to lose one pound of fat. The impression is that such exercise has to be done during one long session. You cannot lose a large amount of weight quickly by exercising. You can lose fat over the long haul by exercising regularly. Jogging for twenty minutes a day, seven days a week, over a one-year period will allow you to shed more than 20 pounds.

SPOT REDUCTION

There is a widely held myth that exercising the muscles in a particular area of the body will remove fat from that area. This is called **spot reduction**. There is no such thing as spot reduction. Exercising will only tone up or strengthen the muscles in a specific area.

INCREASED APPETITE

Another myth is that an increase in physical activity automatically creates an increase in appetite. Mild to moderate exercise will in fact decrease the appetite of most people.

GLANDULAR PROBLEMS

A popular myth is that excessive fat is caused by glandular problems. In reality, only a small percentage of people have glandular problems that make it difficult to control fat.

You cannot lose weight overnight by exercising during one long session.

SUMMARY

Heredity plays a role in your physical appearance. Your genetic makeup determines your body type. There are three basic classifications of body type: endomorph (stocky), mesomorph (muscular), and ectomorph (thin).

Body weight is made up of body fluids, lean body mass, and body fat. This is called body composition. Height and weight charts can be misleading because they do not indicate how much of your body weight is lean body mass and how much is body fat.

Weight gain is not always bad. Excessive fat is what should be avoided. Several methods are used for determining the percentage of body fat. Measurements taken with a skinfold caliper are reliable and easy to use. An acceptable percentage of body fat for the average person your age is from 9 to 15 percent for males and from 14 to 21 percent for females.

Weight control is a major health problem. Fat children and fat teenagers are more likely to become fat adults. Excessive body fat can contribute to a number of health problems, including high blood pressure, heart disease, stroke, diabetes, and kidney disorders, as well as reduced self-image.

Weight loss or gain can be achieved by (1) changing caloric intake, (2) changing caloric output, or (3) a combination of the two. To maintain weight, your caloric intake (what you eat) should be the same as your average daily caloric output (what you burn up). Permanent weight control is best achieved by a combined program of proper nutrition and regular exercise.

STUDY QUESTIONS

VOCABULARY MATCHING

Place the letter of the correct answer in the space provided.

........1. Creeping obesity
........2. Lean body mass
........3. Obese
........4. Somatotypes
........5. Overweight
........6. Bulimia
........7. Long-haul concept
........8. Ideal body weight
........9. Anorexia nervosa
........10. Skinfold caliper

A. Excessive accumulation of body fat
B. Muscle tissue, bones, ligaments, and tendons
C. Exceeds desirable body weight by 10 percent according to height and weight charts
D. Gaining fat very slowly over a period of years
E. Slow, gradual weight reduction
F. Physical classifications of the human body
G. Self-imposed state characterized by severe weight loss
H. Disorder in which one eats excessively, then induces vomiting
I. Your weight with an acceptable percentage of body fat
J. An instrument used to measure amount of body fat

TRUE-FALSE

Circle "T" for all correct statements and "F" for all incorrect ones.

T F 11. A square body with hard, rugged, prominent muscles best describes a pure ectomorph.

T F 12. Staying lean is more difficult for individuals with endomorphic characteristics.

T F 13. How much you weigh is as important as your actual body composition.

T F 14. An acceptable percentage of body fat for teenagers is from 9 to 15 percent for males and from 14 to 21 percent for females.

T F 15. The most accurate method for testing body fat is with a skinfold caliper.

T F 16. There is a close association between overweight people and heart disease.

T F 17. Body fat weighs more than an equal amount of lean body mass.

T F 18. Fat children and fat teenagers are more likely to be fat adults.

T F 19. Anorexia nervosa is a disorder in which the individual eats excessively, then induces vomiting.

T F 20. Increased exercise is usually followed by an increase in appetite.

DISCUSSION

21. Why are height and weight charts not very useful standards?
22. What is the difference between actual body weight and ideal body weight?
23. Explain why many adults and youth in the United States are overweight.
24. Explain how you would lose weight, gain weight, or maintain your weight.
25. Why is the combination of sound nutrition and regular exercise the most desirable method for permanent weight control?

STRESS

11

CHAPTER OBJECTIVES

As you read this chapter, look for answers to these key questions:

- What is stress and why do some of your peers react differently to a specific situation than you?

- What are the common causes of stress?

- What are the effects of stress on the body?

- How do positive stress and negative stress affect you as an individual?

- What are the components of a stress management program?

- What are stress diversion activities and how are they helpful?

- What are negative coping techniques and why should you avoid them?

VOCABULARY

When you have completed this chapter, you should understand the meaning of these vocabulary terms:

- stress
- positive stress (eustress)
- negative stress (distress)
- stressor
- homeostasis
- fight or flight response
- general adaptation syndrome
- stimulus
- adrenaline
- time management
- stress diversion activities
- positive coping strategies
- negative coping techniques

Most people are about as happy as they make up their minds to be.

ABRAHAM LINCOLN

CASE STUDY: SAMMY'S STORY

The school year was only two weeks old, but Sammy was already frustrated, confused, and lost. He felt as if he was drowning. Sammy was in the ninth grade at Midway High School, and he didn't know anyone. During the summer, he and his family had moved to Midway from a smaller town. The middle school he had attended last year was small, and Sammy knew all of the students and teachers. He received personal attention in his classes, which enabled him to do well and receive excellent grades. He was also active in after-school activities and was particularly a standout in athletics.

During the first two weeks at Midway High, Sammy did not find or experience any of the positive things that made him enjoy school in the past. The classes were large and the teachers were too busy to give students individual attention. The football coach discouraged him from coming out for the team because he was too small, didn't know the system, and would have trouble adjusting.

Sammy did not know anyone, and no one knew him. The school was very large, very crowded, and it seemed to Sammy, very noisy. It seemed that all of the other students had their own peer groups with no room for new people. Students smoked openly at

Many teenagers feel a great deal of loneliness, even in a crowd. This is especially true when they are placed in a new situation.

Midway, popped pills, and drank alcohol. Half of the students spent most of the time high on one drug or another. In fact, these were the only students who showed any interest in him and freely offered him different types of drugs. Although he always turned them down, he found himself thinking that if he accepted their offer just once, maybe he would make friends and be accepted. But that thought scared him. Could he accept only once?

At home, Sammy's family was just as confusing. Everyone had his or her own problems adjusting to new jobs, new friends, new everything. There did not seem to be the time or the interest to listen to Sammy's problems at school. His mother passed it off as a period of

Sammy's feelings of loneliness in his new school are common. We all need friends to talk to and share with.

adjustment. Sammy felt himself withdrawing. He was floating through school, and at the end of the day he could not remember any details. He remembered only an increasingly desperate feeling.

WHAT'S WRONG WITH SAMMY?

Sammy is experiencing stress from many sources. He does not understand what is happening to him. He has never heard of stress or the causes of stress. He does not know what coping strategies (techniques of dealing with stress) are or how to use them. If Sammy does not receive help with his stress soon, it is likely he will begin protecting himself by using whatever means are easy or available to him. Withdrawal, negative behavior, and drug abuse are all unconscious and common reactions to stress. Sammy's new life has him in a pressure cooker and the pressure is building. Sammy needs help or the pressure will build to a point of explosion. The help Sammy needs may be the friendship of people, or it may be the knowledge of what is happening to him and how he can deal with it in a positive manner.

When we feel alone, we will often accept the friendship of anyone who offers it. We should be careful that we do not choose a group of friends who have a set of values that are not acceptable.

WHAT IS STRESS?

Stress is the nonspecific response of the body to any demand made upon it and may vary from one individual to another. It may be caused by both good things (a good grade on a test) and bad things (getting cut from a team). Therefore, stress can be either good or bad, depending on how you and your body react to the specific demand.

If stress results from something good and you react to it in a positive manner, the stress is good. Good stress, or positive stress, is called **eustress**. If stress is caused by something bad or if you react to a given situation in a negative manner, the stress is bad for you. Bad stress, or negative stress, is called **distress**.

INDIVIDUALS REACT DIFFERENTLY TO STRESS

Different people react to the same demand differently. Some people may receive negative stress when the teacher calls on them in class, while others receive positive stress from having the opportunity to answer questions in class. Therefore, you can see that stress is specific to each individual. How you react to a specific demand may be different from the reaction of any of your friends or classmates. This does not mean that you are abnormal. It just means that you are an individual, and that is good.

THE IMPORTANCE OF UNDERSTANDING STRESS

It is not unusual that Sammy does not understand what is happening to him. He does not know about stress and its causes, or how to deal with new or different sources of stress. Most people, adults as well as teenagers, do not understand or are not even aware of stress and the consequences of negative stress. Those who are aware of stress think of it only as negative. If teenagers and parents understood stress, they could help each other.

WHAT CAUSES STRESS?

Situations that cause stress are referred to as **stressors**. Nearly everything is a stressor, creating either positive stress (eustress) or negative stress (distress). Every activity encountered stresses you, with each activity creating a different degree of stress. Some of these activities cause you negative stress, and some cause you positive stress. You may experience positive stress while your best friend may experience negative stress from the same activity because you are different individuals.

Extreme heat and cold temperatures cause the **homeostasis** (internal balance) of your body to be upset. This is a negative physical stressor that requires a physical response. However, extreme temperatures can also cause mental stress.

The death of a person who is close to you requires both a physical and a mental response. The death of a family member may even be a positive stressor. For example, death may occur after the person has been ill for a long time.

POTENTIAL CAUSES OF STRESS

You have many potential sources of stress that bombard you every day. These may include family relationships, school work, peer groups, discrimination, injury, sickness, or fatigue. These stressors can generate both positive stress and negative stress. How you handle or react to these stressors determines their effect on your body and your lifestyle.

ARE ALL CHANGES STRESSORS?

Yes. Even pleasant changes in your daily routine can cause stress. This type of stressor does not cause as great a stress as a bad change, but the body still needs to make an adjustment and use up some of its energy reserve. An example of this is a summer vacation or a holiday season. Many people feel physically tired at the end of their vacation, even though it was enjoyable. This fatigue is caused by the body using up its energy reserve to make all of the adjustments to changes in its normal routine. A good change (vacation) does not create as much negative stress as a bad change (death in family, divorce). But if you are not aware that the situation is stressful, you may let it affect you negatively and ruin your vacation.

MAJOR STRESSORS COME IN MANY FORMS

Major changes in your life are the real negative stressors for which you need to plan coping techniques in order to handle them positively. Sammy's family moved, a change that frequently creates a great deal of negative stress in all family members. This is true even if such a move is caused by something positive such as a promotion that requires a parent to move to another city.

If a family like Sammy's is required to move, an adjustment in the behavior of all family members should be expected. This change in behavior occurs even though the move is due to a positive reason. If the move is regarded as a negative situation, the emotional response will be even greater. Children often think a family move is negative because they have to move away from friends and a comfortable, secure environment. Although all family members are expected to act in a calm, mature manner, some may in fact feel anger and resentment toward other members of the family or their employers. Children frequently let this kind of resentment against their parents build.

Moving from one community or town to another is a major change and usually causes all members in the family a great deal of negative stress, even if the long-term results may be positive.

177

If the threat of stress caused by the move is managed in an appropriate manner, the resulting response will be positive rather than negative. But if no satisfactory way can be found to cope with the stress, those involved will feel increasingly angry and resentful. This continued buildup of stress will cause a weakening of the body systems.

HOW DOES YOUR BODY REACT TO STRESS?

Your body responds physiologically in exactly the same manner to both positive and negative stress. The body's response to a specific stressor occurs in a sequence of three steps, or stages. This sequence is known as the **general adaptation syndrome**. The first stage is the alarm stage. The body makes an immediate response to a stressor, anticipating change and perceiving change as a danger or an emergency. During the second stage, the body learns, or tries to learn, to adapt to the stressor, or it goes through a stage of resistance. The third stage, exhaustion, occurs when the body uses up the energy reserves required for coping with stress.

FIGHT OR FLIGHT RESPONSE

Initiation of the alarm stage occurs when the body receives a **stimulus**, such as one of your parents yelling at you for not carrying out the garbage. This stimulus immediately activates the nervous system which releases adrenaline into the body. **Adrenaline** is the chemical that gives you energy to perform physical acts in an emergency. By increasing the supply of adrenaline, the body moves into the fight or flight mode. A **fight or flight response** is your body's natural protective technique. Every stressor whether positive or negative causes the same thing to happen in your body. The amount of adrenaline released depends on the strength of the stimuli and your previous experience with that stressor.

GLYCOGEN + FAT _____ ENERGY

The "Fight or Flight" response causes many changes to occur in the body. These changes are the same for both positive and negative stress.

The release of additional adrenaline causes body functions to change. The more important changes include the following:

1. Blood circulation is increased to provide your brain, lungs, and muscles with more nutrients (fuel for energy).

2. Nutrients (energy supplies) in the blood are increased.

3. Muscles are strengthened to respond to the fight or flight response.

4. Breathing becomes more rapid to give you more oxygen.

5. Your senses become more alert; for example, the pupils of your eyes dilate to sharpen vision.

HOW DOES YOUR MIND REACT TO STRESS?

You respond to stress both physically and mentally. Your mental response usually involves such emotions as happiness, joy, fear, and anger. The mental or emotional changes you exhibit in response to a stressor actually control how you respond physically. If the emotions caused by the stressor are strong enough, you will undergo a change in behavior.

The psychological (mental) changes in behavior that occur due to an emotional response to stress can be classified as follows:

1. **Rationalizing:** Making up reasons why the situation turned out the way it did, rather than the way it should have.

2. **Projecting:** Blaming someone else for your own faults.

3. **Compensation:** Over-reacting to make up for a feeling of inadequacy.

4. **Avoidance:** Refusing to act on a situation.

Permitting yourself to practice these mental responses to negative stress will lead you to more serious problems.

Although they are common, these forms of behavior are not considered healthy. If they are not corrected, they can lead to more serious mental disturbances.

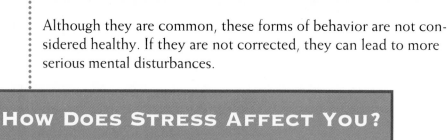

HOW DOES STRESS AFFECT YOU?

As you know by now, stress has both positive and negative effects. The manner in which you respond to the stress, both physically and mentally, determines whether the immediate and long-term effects of stress will be positive or negative.

The degree to which stress affects you physically is also determined by what you are doing when you receive the stimuli from a stressor and the additional adrenaline is released. If you are physically active when the adrenaline is released, it is easier for you to deal with the stress because the exercise burns up the additional supply of adrenaline and allows body functions (such as heart rate and blood pressure) to return to normal. This will not happen if you are sitting. When sitting, the body reacts to the stressor in the very same manner that it would if you were active, except that the adrenaline is not burned up quickly. The adrenaline remains in the body system for a long period of time, keeping body functions at an unusually high level. If your blood pressure is frequently elevated by stress and not subsequently lowered by exercise, you could develop high blood pressure.

POSITIVE STRESS (EUSTRESS)

Stress affects you in a positive manner every day. It can provide you with the energy and motivation to accomplish things you want to do or have been demanded of you. Positive stress makes you more creative, alert, aggressive, and dedicated to a task. Positive stress keeps you from becoming bored and fatigued with your daily tasks. By helping you resist fatigue and boredom, positive stress makes you feel good about yourself. It makes you alert and happy, not nervous or uptight. Your peers view you as feeling good about yourself.

NEGATIVE STRESS (DISTRESS)

Too much stress can have a negative affect and can interfere with school work, home life, and your relationship to your peers. It can even lead to health problems over an extended period of time. The effects of negative stress can pile up on you. They act on you in combination, not as individual stressors. Sammy has many different stressors affecting him. He has to deal with the total effect of all stressors. If you are in a situation like Sammy's and you reach the point where you cannot deal with the accumulated effect of all

Physical activity will help burn up adrenalin that is released in a stressful situation.

the stressors, you are suffering from a condition commonly called burnout.

WHAT ARE THE EFFECTS OF NEGATIVE STRESS?

The effect of negative stress (distress) can be set at three different levels. Each level has different symptoms and is more serious than the previous one.

Level one: This level is the least severe. The symptoms include short periods of irritability, fatigue, worry, and frustration.

Level two: The symptoms for this level are similar to the symptoms of level one, but they last as long as two weeks or more.

Level three: This level is the most serious. If you are experiencing stress at this level, you may have minor health problems, such as frequent colds, headaches, dizziness, or diarrhea.

The conditions at level three can develop into severe health problems if they go unattended. These conditions include ulcers, high blood pressure, asthma, and diabetes.

DEVELOPING A STRESS MANAGEMENT PROGRAM

What should you do about negative stress? You need to develop your own stress management program in order to resist the consequences of negative stress. This program should include building up your resistance to negative stress and developing techniques for avoiding negative stress, as well as developing positive coping strategies that will help you deal with the distress you cannot avoid.

DO NOT WORRY ABOUT LITTLE THINGS

WRONG RESPONSE

RIGHT RESPONSE

Remaining calm in situations like this will help you remain alert and let you feel better.

The first step in developing a stress management plan is to stop fighting things that usually cause you a lot of negative stress. You need to allow simple or minor demands on the body (minor stressors) to pass without concern. Such minor stressors might be what happens to you when you drive a car (someone cuts in front of you), spill a glass of milk (the responses of family members), or meet new people (who are probably as nervous as you are). You need to learn to respond to these minor stressors in a positive way.

If you do not respond to minor stressors in a positive manner, your irritation level will build to a point where you will be unable to deal with the impact of a major stressor in a reasonable manner. You do not want to use up your daily energy reserve on minor stressors.

GET FIT

The second step of a good stress management program is to work at developing a greater energy reserve. This can be done by maintaining a high level of physical fitness. This will give you greater energy and help keep you from becoming fatigued as the demands of the day begin to wear you down. We (all) become more irritable and susceptible to minor stressors when we are tired.

YOU ARE WHAT YOU EAT

Proper diet is also part of your fitness and stress management program. A proper diet will help you feel good and look good. Certain aspects of your diet may increase your susceptibility to stress. Sugar and caffeine are two components of most people's diet that are high stressors. Chocolate, colas, coffee, and tea have high concentrations of caffeine. Many prepared foods have high levels of sugar. You should attempt to limit your intake of these items. This will help keep you from becoming irritable, uptight, and unable to cope with even minor stressors.

DEVELOP POSITIVE COPING STRATEGIES

The next step in building your stress management program should be the development of **positive coping strategies** to be used in dealing with stressors you cannot avoid. Each person must have his or her own coping techniques. What is a stress release for your best friend may be a stressor for you.

TEMPORARY RELIEF MAY BE HELPFUL

The first approach to coping with distress is to get some temporary relief. You can do this through exercise, yoga, medicine, or just plain daydreaming. There are a number of relaxation techniques that are very helpful. Learn at least one relaxation technique and practice it daily. Exercise is a good way to burn off adrenaline.

RECOGNIZE EARLY SYMPTOMS OF STRESS

A second approach to developing coping techniques is learning to recognize the early symptoms of stress. You can learn how you physically respond to stress and how to use those physical responses as an early warning of negative stress. If you find your jaw or facial muscles becoming tired you might be reacting to stress by clenching your teeth. This physical symptom, once identified, can be used as a warning signal that you need to take a short break. Other common physical symptoms include tight neck muscles, eye strain, shoulder or back stiffness, and increased heart rate. Do you recognize any of these symptoms in yourself?

IDENTIFY STRESSFUL SITUATIONS

Another important step in developing positive coping strategies is identifying common stressful situations and defining how you nor-

STRESSORS   STRESS MANAGEMENT

You must keep your stress scale balanced.

mally respond to them. Once you have done this, you can modify your reaction or concentrate on replacing your usual response with a more positive response, or coping strategy.

SUPPORT GROUPS ARE HELPFUL

At times, you will be faced with stressful situations that you cannot handle by yourself. In those situations, you will need a support group, people to whom you can talk about a particular stressor. Developing a variety of support groups, such as parents, friends at school, teachers, coaches, or counselors, can be very helpful, regardless of what caused you to become uptight or tense. There will be things you may not feel comfortable talking to your parents about, but you may feel free to discuss them with a peer or a physical education teacher. The more support groups you develop, the better you will feel.

You cannot cope with stress by yourself. You need support groups, such as close friends, school teachers, or family members.

GOAL SETTING

Wise and effective goal setting, as discussed in Chapter 3, is also an important aspect of successful stress management. This is true whether you are dealing with school, work, leisure time, or your social life. Many people become frustrated and burned out from being involved in too many activities where there is little satisfaction or the expectations are unreasonable. Unreasonable expectations may mean too little is expected (you become bored) or too much is expected (you become frustrated). Get involved in a variety of activities that will challenge you. If you have a positive attitude and put forth a good effort, you will experience success. These types of activities are positive stressors. However, do not get involved in activities that are beyond your abilities, or in so many activities that you do not have time to devote the effort required to be successful. Getting in over your head, so that failure is almost a certainty is a negative stressor.

TIME MANAGEMENT

Learning to organize your time, or **time management**, is an important stress management technique. Having too many demands made on you is a common cause of negative stress. Therefore, do not get involved in too many activities. Learn to say no. Get involved in activities that are challenging, within your abilities, and within your time limit. Time management may involve setting up time schedules that you follow regardless of what comes up: a time to do homework, a time for physical activity, and a time to watch television. Another technique may be keeping a priority list of things that need to be accomplished each day. The pressure of time is a major stressor for most people. How well you manage your time will determine how well you manage the stress in your life.

STRESS DIVERSION ACTIVITIES

Stress diversion activities are either active or passive activities that help you reduce or divert stress. You should especially try to fill your leisure time with activities that are vigorous enough to provide some of the training effects discussed earlier. These types of activities provide two benefits: (1) they burn up the extra adrenaline caused by stressors to prepare you for the fight or flight response which allows physiological functions (heart rate, blood pressure, breathing rate) to return to normal following the exercise; (2) they improve your level of fitness preventing you from becoming easily fatigued which enables you to better cope with negative stressors. Remember, as you become fatigued, you also become more irritable and, therefore, more susceptible to negative stress.

Quiet, passive activities are also good stress diversion activities. These types of activities help you forget about stressors that are bothering you. Watching television, reading a book, or listening to music may all be good stress diversion activities if they help you relax and focus on positive things.

Remember that what is stress diversion for your friend may be a stressor for you. If you are highly competitive and concerned with winning or losing, any competitive game or activity may be a stressor. If that is the case, you need to choose a noncompetitive activity as your stress diversion activity.

Positive coping techniques can be summarized in the following list:

1. high level of physical fitness
2. proper diet
3. awareness of your reaction to distress
4. awareness of common stressors
5. relaxation techniques
6. involvement in challenging activities
7. support groups
8. time management

NEGATIVE COPING TECHNIQUES YOU SHOULD AVOID

Negative responses, or **negative coping techniques**, are those responses you use to ease or disguise the symptoms of stress. These techniques are harmful not only to you but also to the people around you. Most of these negative techniques can be grouped into four categories: excessive emotion, impatience, avoidance, and use of drugs and alcohol.

BEING OVEREMOTIONAL DOES NOT HELP

Sometimes an emotional outburst is the only response a person can make to negative stress.

A common reaction to negative stress is an overemotional one, particularly when your feelings, ego, or self-esteem are threatened. Stress causes a fight or flight response. Most of the time it is not appropriate for you to fight physically and you cannot run away, so the fight or flight response becomes an emotional attempt to protect yourself or your self-esteem. A common response to criticism is to charge emotionally, "It's not my fault." This type of response is particularly common when the accumulated pressure of a large number of negative stressors begins to wear you down, fatigue you, or cause you to become irritable. Many times people blurt out negative statements (emotionally) they really do not believe or even want to say. These negative comments may hurt the feelings of people or generate emotional responses from them. Practice a number of positive coping strategies as a way of helping yourself avoid this negative technique.

DO NOT BE IMPATIENT

You may become impatient with yourself or with others. Impatience may occur when you become involved in activities in which your abilities are not challenged or in activities that are far too difficult. You may also experience impatience when you become involved in too many activities. Proper goal setting and appropriate selection of activities are important if you are going to offset the threat of impatience.

AVOIDANCE MAY NOT BE THE ANSWER

Although avoiding certain stressful situations is a positive coping technique, there are times when withdrawal or avoiding a stressor is not good. If you are afraid to talk with strangers and avoid such stressful situations, you may not meet or get to know that boy or girl whom you really would like to meet and know. By avoiding that stressful situation, you are limiting your peer group and negatively affecting your lifestyle choices.

Avoiding certain stressful situations, like talking to someone of the opposite sex, can cause you to miss rewarding and positive experiences, thus limiting your lifestyle choices.

If talking in class is very stressful to you, you may choose to avoid that stressor by not volunteering or, when called upon, saying you do not know. This may not be appropriate if your grade is partly determined by your participation in class. Avoiding this stressor is also negative, since you are not learning to handle this situation properly. It is important that you learn to deal with this problem since all people, from time to time, find themselves in a situation in which they need to talk with or in front of peers. Depending on their occupations, some people need to do this more than others. If you choose to avoid this situation and never learn to deal with it, you will place limits on yourself in social situations and in your job. To avoid speaking in front of groups may be viewed as negative. This practice has even kept people from accepting good jobs for which they were qualified. You should not let a stressor control your lifestyle choices.

DRUGS AND ALCOHOL ARE NOT THE ANSWER

The fourth category of negative coping strategies is the use of drugs or alcohol. Some adults have a couple of drinks every day to relax after work. Drugs and alcohol can cause physical and mental problems, be habit forming, and may cause an individual to lose efficiency and motivation. Exercise and relaxation techniques work better than drugs or alcohol and have the double benefit of relaxation and increasing resistance to stress. Drugs and alcohol only cover up your stress and lower your resistance to stress.

Drugs and alcohol will not eliminate stressors, but will keep you from positively coping with your problems.

SUMMARY

Stress is the nonspecific response of the body to any demand made upon it. Stress may be either good or bad. Many factors cause stress. What may cause stress for you may not cause the same reaction in your friend.

Nearly everything you encounter is a stressor; some are positive and some negative. All changes cause stress, even the pleasant ones, but major changes cause the major stressors.

The body's response is the same for both positive and negative stress. Responses to stress will be both physical and mental. Many of these changes can have serious effects if left unattended.

In order to deal with stress, you need to practice positive coping strategies. Having a high level of physical fitness, eating properly, and being involved in challenging activities will help you handle your stress. Active and passive stress diversion activities may also help you cope with stressors.

The use of negative coping techniques can be dangerous. Negative methods of dealing with stress only cover up the effects of stress and do not deal with the stressor. Emotional outbursts, impatience, avoidance, or the use of drugs or alcohol are all negative coping techniques.

STUDY QUESTIONS

MATCHING

Place the letter of the correct answer in the space provided.

.............1. Adrenaline
.............2. Coping techniques
.............3. Diversion
.............4. Fight or flight
.............5. Homeostasis
.............6. Bad stress
.............7. Physiological
.............8. Good stress
.............9. Psychological
.............10. Stimulus
.............11. Stress
.............12. Stressors

A. Eustress
B. Distress
C. Things that cause stress
D. A signal to your body that a change has happened or is about to happen
E. Chemical in the body that gives you added energy
F. Mental or emotional reaction to stress
G. Biological or physical response to stress
H. Ways that you deal with stress
I. The body's response to a demand made of it
J. The body's response to negative stress
K. Shielding from or reflecting the effects of stress
L. Internal balance or biological balance of the body

TRUE-FALSE

Circle "T" for all correct statements and "F" for all incorrect ones.

T F 13. Stress is the nonspecific response of the body to any demand made upon it.

T F 14. Stress is always present.

T F 15. Eustress is positive stress that helps you perform.

T F 16. Vacations can cause you stress.

T F 17. Changes in your life will cause stress only if they affect you negatively.

T F 18. Your body will react differently to positive and negative stress.

T F 19. Your response to stress is only physical, not mental.

T F 20. You are better able to handle stress if you are active.

T F 21. Stress can cause you to become physically ill.

T F 22. Coping strategies can be either positive or negative.

T F 23. You should let some minor stressors pass without concern.

T F 24. Avoidance should never be a part of your stress management program.

T F 25. Sugar and caffeine may cause you to be more irritable and less able to cope with minor stress.

T F 26. It is all right to use coping techniques that mask or hide stress.

DISCUSSION

27. Identify and discuss the different stressors that Sammy is facing.

28. Describe the negative coping strategies Sammy could use in dealing with his stress.

29. Discuss how you can identify stressful events and how you can better cope with those events.

30. Discuss the benefits of exercise as stress diversion.

CONSUMER ISSUES

12

CHAPTER OBJECTIVES

As you read this chapter, look for answers to these key questions:

- What influences people to buy certain products?

- What is the most powerful tool in combating consumer fraud?

- What are examples of unsound and worthless fitness products?

- How can a fitness center be evaluated?

- Why are advertisements claiming fast weight reduction and spot reduction fraudulent schemes?

- What are anabolic steroids and why should they be avoided?

- How can teenagers combat false advertising claims?

NEW REDUCING PAJAMAS

REDUCE WAIST, HIPS, THIGHS, ETC. WHILE YOU SLEEP!

NO DRUGS!
NO STIMULANTS!
NO HUNGER!

VOCABULARY

When you have completed this chapter, you should understand the meaning of these vocabulary terms:

- consumer
- advertising
- diuretics
- edema
- fraudulent
- anabolic steroids

You can't always judge a book by the cover.

YOU THE CONSUMER

What do you have in common with your neighbors and grandparents, with entertainers and professional athletes? All of you are consumers. A **consumer** is a person who buys goods and services. As a consumer, you have many choices. You can choose what to buy, where to buy, and when to buy. You can also choose to get the best value for your money. By making wise purchasing decisions, you can become a satisfied consumer.

Each year teenagers spend billions of dollars on clothing, records, tapes, magazines, athletic gear, and many other items. In fact, teen spending power is so large that many companies cater only to the teen market. After studying this chapter, you will be better prepared to make wise decisions about spending your money on items, brand names, and services related to physical fitness and sports.

Many companies cater only to the teen market.

WHAT INFLUENCES YOUR BUYING DECISIONS?

What influenced your buying decision when you bought your last pair of jeans? Did you buy the same brand you bought before? Did you buy the brand advertised in the latest issue of a teen magazine? Or was your decision influenced by the brand your friends were wearing?

INFLUENCE OF PEERS

As a teen you are probably influenced by friends when you buy certain items or brand names. You enjoy the feeling of belonging to a group and naturally like to conform to what your friends are

Friends often have a great influence on what you buy.

You say I'll get bigger muscles in three days? Sure, I want one!

Many people waste money on useless products.

doing. While it is fun and natural to follow the crowd, it is important to be sure you are buying what is best for you. When buying an item, ask yourself the following questions:

- Am I buying a fad item that is popular today but will soon be out of fashion?
- Am I getting the best value for my money?
- Am I spending twice as much money for a name-brand item?

INFLUENCE OF HABIT

Buying decisions are frequently influenced by buying habits. You may think that other brands are inferior if you have the habit of always buying name-brand items. You may be missing excellent bargains if you shop at only one store. Try to fight off the tendency to be a consumer snob.

INFLUENCE OF ADVERTISING

Advertising can have a powerful influence on your buying decisions. **Advertising** is found in all types of media that surround you every day. Whatever the form, advertising offers many advantages and lets consumers know which products or services are available. It lets people know about sales, and it introduces new products, along with the benefits of those products. There are also disadvantages to advertising. Sometimes it encourages people to buy things they do not need. It can also be misleading. For example, some ads make exaggerated claims in regard to your physical activity needs.

Some experts believe that television commercials damage young people's self-esteem by portraying people in almost supernatural ways. Do not allow such commercials to convince you that you are neither attractive, nor witty, nor physically capable when compared to people seen in television ads. This is exactly what the advertisers hope for because the products in the commercials then appear to be the solution for people not feeling good about themselves.

HAVE YOU BEEN RIPPED OFF?

Do you like to get ripped off? The obvious answer to this question is NO. While this is true, many people appear ready to buy any product that has some promise of helping them look and feel better. Billions of dollars are spent every year by Americans on questionable products. All of us have been victimized by false advertisements at one time or another, but teenagers are an extremely susceptible group because they have little information and may not be able to separate fact from fiction.

Teenagers have a strong desire to look as good as possible. Because of this, many companies advertise almost anything that promises to help teenagers look more attractive. Teenagers are targets of advertising and, as a result, spend a lot of money on glamour products. However, they are often hindered in their buying decisions by a lack of knowledge.

KNOWLEDGE IS THE KEY

Knowledge is probably the only way to combat false advertising. It does not take much knowledge to be able to spot unethical or worthless claims. You must beware of any treatment, device, or product that is being promoted to make your body more attractive. You need to be especially leery of products or treatments promising amazing results in a very short time. Your body cannot be reshaped overnight.

ARE YOU A KNOWLEDGEABLE CONSUMER?

Physical fitness consumers must be knowledgeable in order to get the greatest benefit from their money. Knowledge is the key to consumer power—your power! You must be able to determine which advertisements are sound and which are unsound. People selling unsound products do not want you to be knowledgeable about the real effects of their products. They would much rather have you believe what you see, hear, or read about the thousands of products on the market. The end result is that they make money, and the uninformed consumer finds very little satisfaction from the products because few of the promised results actually happen.

It is easy to say No to false advertising claims if you have knowledge.

SPOT REDUCTION: THE BIG MYTH

Many people want to lose pounds in one area of the body, such as the stomach or thighs. You may have friends who would like to lose a few pounds in a specific area. In order to lose these pounds, people look to advertisements that promise fast and easy results in spot reduction if they purchase a certain product.

The misconception that fat can be reduced or removed from one specific area of the body is probably the most obvious denial of established knowledge about the way the body responds to exercise. It has been shown through research that spot reduction is impossible. Many people still hold to the idea that exercising an isolated part of the body, where the fat has accumulated, trims fat

NEW REDUCING PAJAMAS

REDUCE WAIST, HIPS, THIGHS, ETC. WHILE YOU SLEEP!

NO DRUGS! NO STIMULANTS! NO HUNGER!

from that specific area. This is simply not true. There is no known means by which fat may be broken down and lost from just one part of your body. If this were true, many people would do what was necessary to trim unsightly fat from their stomachs, hips, or thighs.

Many exercise gadgets, devices, and programs are based on the misconception that if muscle groups beneath the fat are used, the fat will go away. The most prevalent example of this is the belief that sit-ups reduce fat on the stomach. Ask ten of your friends how they would reduce the fat on their stomachs and, in all probability, nine out of ten will answer by saying, "Sit-ups." It is also commonly believed that stretching exercises can be used to get rid of fat in a specific spot. Some of these exercises serve a very useful purpose, but that purpose is not the reduction of fat from a specific part of the body.

FALSE ADVERTISING

Wouldn't you agree that this advertisement is very impressive from the standpoint of sounding easy to do? Imagine! All you have to do is lie down and relax. The rest of the advertisement, a full-page ad not included here, uses such phrases as "will unleash

"Just lie back, relax. You can lose as much weight as you want and never gain any of it back."

unused powers of your subconscious mind," "ignite natural fat burners," "launch an attack on stubborn bulges," "break down the fat on thighs, stomach, and fannys," "shrink the size of your stomach," and finally "get rid of your hunger." Typically, the reader's attention is drawn to the glamorous woman shown in the ad. The final bait thrown out to tempt the buyer is this statement: "If you just send in $19.95 plus $2.00 shipping charge plus tax, you will receive a cassette tape which will guarantee beautiful results, and you can be just as attractive as the young woman in the ad."

EXERCISE GADGETS AND GIMMICKS

A complete list of useless fat-reduction exercise gadgets and products would be extremely long. The following are just a few examples of unsound exercise gadgets and gimmicks.

A. Massage does not break up fat and allow it to be burned off. Massage feels good and may help loosen up tight muscles, but it does not cause weight loss.

B. Vibrating belts and other devices that vibrate or shake to massage a part of your body do not break up fat, help you lose weight, or help improve your physical fitness level.

C. Sauna baths may feel great, but they have no effect on weight loss.

D. Motorized exercise bikes, or any other motorized exercise devices that do all the work, will not cause you to lose weight or help improve your physical fitness level.

E. Plastic or rubberized sweat and sauna suits make people sweat a lot, but they prevent the evaporation of heat from the body and hinder the ability of the body to cool itself. The weight loss that occurs when wearing these items is water loss, not fat loss. After you sweat off a few pounds of body fluids during a vigorous workout, you will regain the weight as soon as you drink fluids.

This machine can not help you lose weight.

Wearing a plastic or rubberized suit can be hazardous to your health.

F. Body wraps have been popular through the years. People selling these products claim that you can lose inches of fat rapidly by wearing them. Some body wraps are soaked in a solution that is supposed to have magical capabilities. There is absolutely no truth to the belief that people can lose weight or increase their physical fitness level by wearing body wraps.

H. Electric stimulators cause a mild electric current to go to a muscle and make it move. Such devices do very little for weight loss or physical fitness, and they could be dangerous to some people.

I. Bust developers have been a popular form of misleading advertising for over a century. It is not surprising that such devices are still popular, since many adult females believe they need to have bigger breasts in order to look more like the females seen in magazines and on television. Certain weight training exercises for the chest may enhance breast appearance by firming up or toning the muscles underneath the breasts, but nothing can be done to increase the size of the breasts.

Appetite suppressants and thyroid hormones are two general categories of drugs commonly used in the treatment of overweight and obese people. These drugs supposedly increase the body's metabolic rate and, therefore, cause the body to burn more calories. Research has shown that only a small percentage of overweight and obese people have a hormone problem. Most have simply developed extremely poor exercise and nutritional habits.

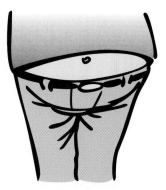

FLAB AWAY
NO APPETITE CONTROL CAPSULE WORKS HARDER TO HELP YOU LOSE WEIGHT.
NEW! EUROPEAN DISCOVERY BY DR. ADIPOSE

WHAT ABOUT DIURETICS?

Diuretics are used to control different types of **edema** (accumulation of fluid in body tissues), congestive heart failure, and high blood pressure. They are occasionally prescribed for women with high blood pressure who experience weight gain due to water retention before their menstrual period. Diuretics do not promote real weight loss. Any weight lost returns with your first glass of water. Diuretics may be dangerous for the following reasons. They may:

- lead to a dangerously low potassium level, which can cause heart problems,
- upset the body's chemical balance,
- increase cardiovascular problems for people with high blood pressure,
- cause blood clotting problems during menstruation,
- damage the kidneys if used continually.

Diuretics are a very poor solution to a weight-gain problem. Again, water loss is not true weight reduction because no calories are burned. Those who use diuretics are only fooling themselves! Do not be an uninformed consumer.

FAD DIETS

Many Americans seem only too willing to pay any price for a quick, simple, and comfortable method of getting rid of their excess body fat. At first glance, it might appear that a number of programs and products on the market could accomplish this, but the fact is that a simple, easy cure for being overweight or obese remains to be discovered. While some diets or remedies may bring about temporary weight reduction, most are not only ineffective but are also hazardous to your health. You should be very skeptical of crash diets recommended in popular diet books, appetite suppressant drugs, and any miracle food that comes with money-back guarantees.

ANABOLIC STEROIDS

Athletes are vulnerable to claims that certain substances can enhance their performance. You have probably heard of the abuse of anabolic steroids by body builders, professional football players, and track athletes. Many other people experiment with these substances in an effort to improve their physical appearance or to become stronger. Research studies indicate that teenagers are also using steroids more frequently. It is extremely important that teenagers understand the very serious side effects of the use of anabolic steroids.

WHAT ARE ANABOLIC STEROIDS?

Anabolic steroids are a synthetic version of testosterone, the male sex hormone. Synthetic anabolic steroids are complex chemicals that the body does not handle easily or naturally. Synthetic anabolic steroids are similar to testosterone in chemical structure, but they affect the body differently.

EFFECTS OF ANABOLIC STEROIDS ON THE BODY

The male testes produce testosterone naturally. At puberty, males may have as much as a twentyfold increase in testosterone naturally. Testosterone stimulates the growth of bone, muscle, and hair, as well as affects emotional development.

If anabolic steroids are administered orally or by injection, the body shuts down its own production of testosterone. The body reacts this way because it recognizes that it already has more than an adequate supply of testosterone. The testicles will shrink if anabolic steroids are taken for a long period of time, since the testosterone-producing cells in the body are no longer active.

Say NO to steroids.

These drugs are extremely dangerous to anyone taking them. The following are some of the undesirable side effects associated with steroid use.

POSSIBLE SIDE EFFECTS OF STEROID USE

- liver and kidney damage
- decrease in ultimate height
- increased risk of cancer
- scalp hair loss
- appearance of acne
- decrease in size of the testicles and impotency
- increased aggression and unpredictable mood changes
- reduction of breast size in women

Young people have more problems with anabolic steroids than older people. One reason has to do with the difference in bone growth. These drugs can cause premature closure of the growth plates on the ends of the long bones in your body. This can have a very serious effect on your growth. It can decrease the height to which you would normally grow.

The more a person uses steroids, the greater the risk of developing one of the many conditions identified as harmful side effects. You would be wise to adhere to the position taken by the American College of Sports Medicine. This group recommends that because of the many dangerous side effects everyone should refrain from steroid use. Once again the answer to self-improvement is not found in a pill or a bottle.

ARE HEALTH CLUBS WORTH THE MONEY?

The number of fitness centers has expanded rapidly in recent years, since more and more people have become conscious of their fitness and appearance. Your decision to join a fitness center may depend on such factors as cost and your personal needs.

Most fitness centers conduct an orientation session in the use of the exercise equipment and make an effort to develop a personal fitness program to meet individual needs. In most cases, these orientation sessions are conducted by knowledgeable people. Occasionally, however, instructors have little knowledge about how to exercise properly. For your own protection and your own best development, sensitize your mind about certain exercise myths, such as spot reduction. If you detect that instructors have a lack of knowledge, look for another fitness center.

By learning all you can about your body and which exercises are best, you will not need anyone telling you what to do. You may

Use objective criteria to evaluate a fitness center. Do not let the glitter or a high-pressure salesperson influence you.

not even need to join a health club or fitness center. Do some comparative shopping if you decide to join a fitness center. These centers frequently have specials, and you may be able to save considerable amounts of money. It is a common practice, however, to try to get you to sign up for a multiyear agreement, with the bait being that then your average yearly fee would be less than if you joined for just one year. It is strongly advised that you avoid this type of agreement. Although it may sound like a good deal, you may later stop using the health club and end up spending a large amount of money for a short-term use.

TIPS ON IDENTIFYING FALSE ADVERTISING

Here are a few more tips to help you recognize unsound advertisements.

A. Beware of testimonials. Have you ever wondered why so many people offer testimonials for various products? You are right if your answer is money. The people who make the testimonials are paid by the companies who make the products. Are there good testimonials? Sometimes, but you must read or listen carefully to their claims. You should also be wary of your friends who talk about products that have helped them lose fat in just three days or some similar claim.

B. The offer generally involves a special gift for fast action. If it sounds too good to be true, it probably is.

C. The location of the ad may be another tip-off. An unsound ad is usually placed in the back of a magazine.

D. Is it likely that one product can do everything? No! One product cannot do everything although it is easy to find advertisements that make this claim.

THIS PRODUCT IS UNBELIEVABLE - I LOST 5 LBS. IN ONE HOUR!

Beware of testimonials!

In the free-enterprise system that we have in this country, people are allowed and even encouraged to start small businesses that provide services to others. They need to advertise to promote the sale of their services, but a few get greedy for quick money and make exaggerated claims about their products. The claims for these products are referred to as being **fraudulent** because the product does not accomplish what is claimed.

The Federal Trade Commission and the Food and Drug Administration are unable to effectively regulate the sale of fraudulent weight-reducing schemes, since companies are not required to provide evidence of their beneficial claims prior to public sale of their products.

WHAT CAN YOU DO TO COMBAT FALSE ADVERTISING?

You may wonder how you can stop false advertising if government agencies are slow and at times ineffective. There are things that you can do as an individual or in a group (teens) to combat false advertising. Many people who are trying to make a living from the sale of useless products assume that teenagers are not smart enough to filter through the big words and fancy promises and recognize that certain products are worthless. They are in for a surprise!

You can become an advocate for teenage consumerism. Tell your friends about the advertisements. Write letters to the editors of the various magazines, criticizing products that are being falsely advertised. Call your local Better Business Bureau, and explain why you believe the advertising for a particular product is fraudulent.

Everyone wants to look and feel as good as possible. There are no easy methods to accomplish these goals. Neither pills nor diets nor secret formulas will do the trick.

Be a smart shopper! Control your money carefully, and remember that the knowledge you have gained is power in your pocket. Use it wisely.

Be a responsible consumer. Take action when you have been exposed to a false claim.

SUMMARY

Hundreds of unsound products are sold every year to consumers who want to be more physically attractive. People selling these products are experts in making you believe you can improve yourself, usually in a very short period of time. They are successful in selling worthless products because many consumers do not have the necessary knowledge to recognize false statements. You can protect yourself, your family, and your friends from being ripped off by understanding some basic information related to how the body reacts to exercise and proper health practices. You can become a strong and effective advocate for sound advertising and play an important role in getting worthless products off the shelves of your local stores.

TRUE-FALSE

Circle the "T" for all correct statements and the "F" for all incorrect ones.

T F 1. Companies often target teenagers in order to sell personal improvement products.

T F 2. People selling useless products want the consumers to be knowledgeable about products that have to do with looking and feeling good.

T F 3. You can reduce or remove fat from specific areas of your body by exercising that area.

T F 4. Doing "sit-ups" removes fat from a person's stomach.

T F 5. Massage helps a person to become physically fit.

T F 6. Motorized exercise devices that do all of the work will not cause you to lose weight or help you to improve your fitness level.

T F 7. Wearing a rubberized sweat suit in hot weather can be very dangerous.

T F 8. Research has shown that a large percentage of overweight people have hormone problems.

T F 9. Diuretics may upset the body's chemical balance.

T F 10. Fluid loss through the use of diuretics is a permanent weight loss.

T F 11. A good way to tell whether or not a product is sound is to read the personal testimonials.

T F 12. Teenagers can help get unsound products off the market.

T F 13. Knowledge can help you save money and keep you from buying worthless products.

T F 14. The general use of anabolic steroids is considered drug abuse.

T F 15. The use of anabolic steroids can cause a decrease in the normal height to which you would grow.

DISCUSSION

16. Identify something that you purchased recently. What influenced you to buy the item? What influenced you to buy from that specific store? Was a brand name involved? If so, what influenced you to buy that brand name?

17. A friend is concerned about his fat stomach and tells you he is doing sit-ups to get rid of the fat. You immediately know he is on the wrong track. What should you tell him? Of what value are sit-ups?

18. Your mother is concerned about her legs because they are getting flabby. She asks you if flexibility exercises could do her any good. What is your answer? What type of exercise would be important for her to do? What other factor might be of extreme importance?

19. Your girlfriend wants to join a health club and she does not know which one to join. How can you advise her?

20. It would appear that those persons who direct companies that produce questionable products believe teenagers are not intelligent consumers. What can teens do to counter this belief?

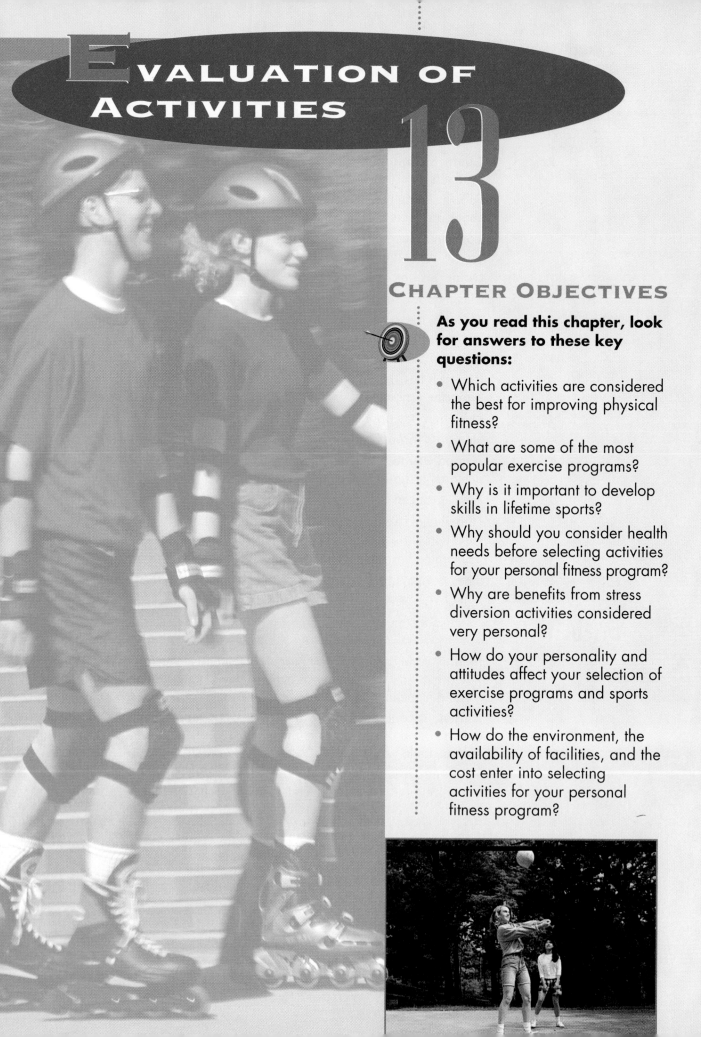

EVALUATION OF ACTIVITIES

13

CHAPTER OBJECTIVES

As you read this chapter, look for answers to these key questions:

- Which activities are considered the best for improving physical fitness?

- What are some of the most popular exercise programs?

- Why is it important to develop skills in lifetime sports?

- Why should you consider health needs before selecting activities for your personal fitness program?

- Why are benefits from stress diversion activities considered very personal?

- How do your personality and attitudes affect your selection of exercise programs and sports activities?

- How do the environment, the availability of facilities, and the cost enter into selecting activities for your personal fitness program?

Quality is never an accident; it is always the result of effort.

WHICH ACTIVITIES ARE BEST?

In order to be fit and healthy as well as look good and feel good for a lifetime, you need to engage in some kind of regular exercise program. The key to developing a successful personal fitness program is to know what is right for you. The selection of activities depends, in part, on the answers to these questions.

- Which components of physical fitness do you need to improve most?
- What kind of exercises and activities do you enjoy?
- What kind of activities will help you manage your stress?
- What sports skills do you have?
- Will you be exercising alone or with others?
- Where will you be exercising?
- Will you need special equipment or facilities?

No single physical activity meets the needs of everyone. You have to select activities that best meet your own needs. Try to include a variety of activities in your personal fitness program to avoid boredom and to keep it fun and interesting. Do not be afraid to try a new or different activity; however, do not hesitate to stop doing an

205

activity if you do not enjoy it. Do not become a physical fitness dropout just because you picked the wrong activity. Keep trying until you find activities you really enjoy. You are more likely to exercise regularly if you choose activities you enjoy.

CATEGORIES OF ACTIVITIES

In order to determine the activities that are best for you, you will need to become acquainted with and evaluate the many available exercise programs. Physical activities can be divided into two groups: (1) exercise programs and (2) sports activities.

EXERCISE PROGRAMS

Exercise programs can be designed by you or by someone else. It is important to remember that any exercise program should be based on the principles of training discussed in earlier chapters to assure both benefit and safety.

Exercise programs seen on television and on video tapes are examples of planned programs.

Predetermined programs usually include specific exercises for persons of specific fitness levels or ages. These are sometimes referred to as **planned programs**. Aerobic dance classes, exercise programs seen on television and video tapes, circuit training, and fitness trails found in many recreation parks are examples of planned programs. Your overall personal fitness program should include several different exercise programs in order to meet all your needs. You are encouraged to try different exercise programs. Some sample planned programs are provided to assist you in developing your own program. The following are some of the more popular exercise programs.

AEROBIC DANCE

Aerobic dance is a popular exercise program for people of all ages. Aerobic dance routines include a combination of dance steps and calisthenics done to upbeat popular music. Aerobic dance can be high-impact or low-impact. **High-impact aerobics** include jumping, bouncing, and running. **Low-impact aerobics** include vigorous arm movements while keeping one foot in contact with the ground at all times. You can develop your own aerobic dance routines, participate in programs at health clubs and recreation departments, or follow those seen on television and home video tapes.

Aerobic dance is a popular exercise program for people of all ages.

AQUA DYNAMICS

Aqua dynamics is an exercise program done in the water. You do not have to be a swimmer to participate in this kind of program. Many exercises in aqua dynamics are similar to calisthenics. Because of the buoyancy provided by the water aqua dynamics is a very popular exercise program among handicapped persons and those with injuries.

BICYCLING

Bicycling is one of the most popular exercise programs for developing cardiovascular fitness and muscular endurance in the legs. Bicycling must be done continuously for at least 20 minutes in order to have an aerobic effect. When bicycling, try to maintain steady, continuous pedaling rather than coasting.

Sample Bicycling Program			
Week	Frequency/Wk	Distance	Time
1	3	2.0 miles	12:00
2	3	2.0 miles	10:00
3	3	2.5 miles	13:00
4	3	3.0 miles	20:00
5	4	3.0 miles	20:00

CALISTHENICS

Calisthenics are exercises in which body parts or body weight is the resistance. Such exercises are convenient to do because they require little or no equipment and can be done at home. Calisthenics are used for warm-up, flexibility, and development of muscular strength and muscular endurance. Running in place, side-leg raises, push-ups, sit-ups, and pull-ups are examples of calisthenics.

CIRCUIT TRAINING

Circuit training is an exercise program in which you move around a prescribed course, stopping at stations along the way to perform specified exercises. This exercise program stresses continuous activity. The intensity of a circuit can be made greater by increasing the repetitions of the exercise at each station, by decreasing the time required to complete the circuit, or by a combination of the two.

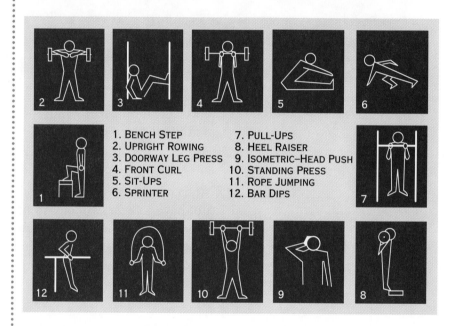

1. BENCH STEP
2. UPRIGHT ROWING
3. DOORWAY LEG PRESS
4. FRONT CURL
5. SIT-UPS
6. SPRINTER
7. PULL-UPS
8. HEEL RAISER
9. ISOMETRIC–HEAD PUSH
10. STANDING PRESS
11. ROPE JUMPING
12. BAR DIPS

FITNESS TRAILS

Fitness trails can be found in many recreation parks and on school grounds. A fitness trail is an established route of considerable distance with exercise stations dispersed along the way. Signs that describe and illustrate each exercise and indicate the number of repetitions are posted at each station. You can walk or jog between stations, stop and perform the exercise at each station, and continue on to the end of the trail.

INTERVAL TRAINING

Interval training is an exercise program involving a series of exercises interspersed with rest periods. Interval training is usually associated with endurance training in running and swimming, but the general principles are applicable to any kind of exercise program. There are four variables in interval training: (1) speed or

An Example of Interval Training Applied to Various Activities					
Activity	Freq./Wk	Distance	Time	Rest	Repetitions
Jogging	3	220 yds.	0:45	2:00	5
Swimming	3	50 yds.	2:00	1:00	6
Bicycling	3	.5 miles	2:00	1:00	8

rate, (2) distance or length of time, (3) rest period, and (4) number of repetitions. One or all of the variables can be altered to change the intensity of the workout.

JOGGING

Jogging is one of the most popular forms of aerobic exercise. Many people believe jogging is the best overall exercise for developing and maintaining cardiovascular fitness. You can jog almost anywhere at almost any time. You can jog alone, with someone, or with a group of people. The only special equipment required is a good pair of running shoes.

Sample Jogging Program			
Week	Frequency/Wk	Distance	Time
1	3	1.0 mile	12:00
2	3	1.5 miles	18:00
3	3	1.5 miles	16:00
4	3	2.0 miles	26:00
5	4	2.0 miles	24:00

ROPE JUMPING

Rope jumping is an excellent cardiovascular fitness activity that requires only a few simple skills and a rope. Many people jump rope when there is no opportunity to jog, swim, or bicycle, such as in a motel room when traveling. In jumping rope, you should use a continuous, progressive routine. Progress very slowly in order to prevent injuries. The length of the rope should be such that it reaches your armpits when held to the ground beneath your feet.

Rope jumping provides a safe means of developing cardiovascular fitness when you are traveling.

SWIMMING

Swimming is an excellent exercise program for developing and maintaining physical fitness. Virtually every muscle is utilized as you propel yourself through the water. Swimming for physical fitness is done in laps at a mild or moderate pace. One advantage that swimming has over other exercise programs is that it is less likely to cause injury.

Sample Swimming Program			
Week	Frequency/Wk	Distance	Time
1	3	300 yds.	12:30
2	3	300 yds.	10:30
3	3	350 yds.	12:00
4	3	350 yds.	12:00
5	4	400 yds.	15:00

If you do not know how to swim, contact your local parks and recreation department, YMCA, or college. These organizations usually offer swimming classes for all ages. You may be surprised at how easy it is to learn to swim.

WALKING

Walking is a very popular form of aerobic exercise. The biggest advantage to walking is that it can be done easily, without wear and tear on the body. You can walk almost anywhere at almost any time. A sturdy, comfortable pair of shoes is the only equipment necessary. When you are walking for physical fitness, do not stroll in a leisurely manner. Instead, walk at a steady pace brisk enough to make your heart beat faster and cause you to breathe more deeply and rapidly.

Sample Walking Program			
Week	Frequency/Wk	Distance	Time
1	3	1.0 mile	15:00
2	3	1.5 miles	22:30
3	3	2.0 miles	30:00
4	3	2.0 miles	26:40
5	4	2.0 miles	26:40

WEIGHT TRAINING

Weight training is considered to be the quickest and most effective way to develop muscular strength and muscular endurance. It is a very popular exercise program among men and is gaining popularity among women, as the myths about femininity and muscle-boundness are discredited. Weight training can be done with either free weights or with machines.

ANALYSIS OF EXERCISE PROGRAMS

Different exercise programs have different benefits. Select the programs that are best for you. The contributions of each exercise program to the health-related components of physical fitness and stress diversion are illustrated in the Exercise Programs Analysis Chart.

Exercise Programs Analysis Chart

Exercise Programs	Flexibility	Cardio-vascular Fitness	Muscular Strength	Muscular Endurance	Body Composition	Stress Diversion	Overall Benefit (Total Points)	Overall Average
Aerobic Dance	3	3	1	2	3	3	15	2.5
Aqua Dynamics	2	2	2	2	2	3	13	2.2
Bicycling	1	3	2	2	3	3	14	2.3
Calisthenics	3	1	2	2	1	3	12	2.0
Circuit Training	2	2	2	3	2	3	14	2.3
Fitness Trails	2	2	2	3	2	3	14	2.3
Interval Training	1	3	2	2	3	3	14	2.3
Jogging	1	3	1	2	3	3	13	2.2
Rope Jumping	1	3	1	2	2	3	12	2.0
Swimming	2	3	2	2	3	3	15	2.5
Walking	1	2	1	2	3	3	12	2.0
Weight Training	2	1	3	3	1	3	13	2.2

Rating Scale: 3—High   2—Medium   1—Low

SPORTS ACTIVITIES

Sports skills activities are those activities that help you develop sports skills and satisfy your need for competition. Some people prefer to get their exercise through participation in sports activities. Some individuals are more easily motivated by sports activities than by other forms of exercise. Keep in mind that even top athletes supplement their sports training with flexibility, cardiovascular, muscular strength, and muscular endurance programs. Whatever sports activities you choose, you will enjoy them more if you have an adequate level of physical fitness.

Your high school years are generally oriented to team or group activities, but as you get older you may lose interest in these activities. You may also experience more difficulty finding opportunities to participate in team activities as you get older. That is why it is important to develop skills in individual sports.

Sports activities may supplement more traditional physical fitness activities.

Individual sports are sometimes called **lifetime sports**, since they can be engaged in for a lifetime. Golf, racquetball, and tennis are examples of such activities. You should develop skills in as many lifetime sports as possible in high school because you can develop new skills more quickly now than later as an adult. Also, the more sports skills you possess, the less limited you will be in your physical activity choices, now and as an adult.

ANALYSIS OF SPORTS ACTIVITIES

Before choosing sports activities to be included in your personal fitness program, you should understand the benefits gained from each activity. Benefits from participation in sports activities vary according to the activity and the skill you possess. Some activities can be very beneficial in meeting your health-related fitness needs if you possess the skill level required to obtain a sufficient workout. The more skill you possess, the greater the benefit will be. Some activities, such as bowling and softball, contribute very little to the development of fitness. Others, such as soccer and basketball, are more conducive to the development of physical fitness.

The contributions of various sports activities on the health-related components of physical fitness and stress diversion are illustrated in the Sports Activities Analysis Chart. The contributions to health-related physical fitness are based upon an individual possessing a reasonable level of skill in the activities. The contributions to stress diversion are based on how a majority of people respond.

It is important to develop skills in lifetime sports.

Sports Activities Analysis Chart

Sports Activities	Flexibility	Cardio-vascular Fitness	Muscular Strength	Muscular Endurance	Body Composition	Stress Diversion	Overall Benefit (Total Points)	Overall Average
Archery	1	1	2	2	1	2	9	1.5
Backpacking/Hiking	2	2	2	3	2	3	14	2.3
Badminton	2	3	1	1	2	1	10	1.7
Basketball	1	3	1	2	3	1	11	1.8
Billiards/Pool	1	1	1	1	1	2	7	1.2
Bowling	1	1	1	1	1	2	7	1.2
Canoeing	1	2	1	2	2	3	11	1.8
Dance (Social)	1	1	1	1	1	3	8	1.3
Diving	3	1	1	1	1	2	9	1.5
Fencing	2	2	1	2	1	1	9	1.5
Football (Flag/Touch)	1	2	1	2	1	1	8	1.3
Golf (Walking)	2	1	1	2	1	1	8	1.3
Gymnastics	3	1	3	3	1	2	13	2.2
Handball/ Paddleball/ Racquetball	2	3	1	2	3	1	12	2.0
Hockey (Field)	2	2	1	2	1	1	9	1.5
Horseback Riding	1	1	1	1	1	3	8	1.3
Judo/Karate	3	1	2	2	1	3	12	2.0
Lacrosse	2	2	1	2	1	1	9	1.5
Rugby	2	3	1	2	1	1	10	1.7
Sailing	2	1	1	1	1	3	9	1.5
Scuba Diving	1	1	1	2	1	3	9	1.5
Skating (Ice/Roller)	1	2	1	2	2	3	11	1.8
Skiing (Cross Country)	1	3	2	2	3	3	14	2.3
Skiing (Downhill)	1	2	2	2	1	3	11	1.8
Soccer	2	3	1	2	3	1	12	2.0
Softball	1	1	1	1	1	2	7	1.2
Speedball	2	2	1	2	1	1	9	1.5
Surfing	2	1	1	2	1	3	10	1.7
Table Tennis	1	1	1	1	1	2	7	1.2
Tennis	2	2	1	1	2	1	9	1.5
Volleyball	2	1	1	1	1	2	8	1.3
Water Polo	3	3	1	3	2	1	13	2.2

Certain factors should affect your decision about which activities will be most beneficial for your personal fitness program. These factors are listed below.

- **health needs**
- **sports skills**
- **stress diversion**
- **personality and attitudes**
- **financial considerations**
- **availability of facilities**
- **environmental considerations**

HEALTH NEEDS

How physically fit are you? Which health-related components of physical fitness do you need to improve the most? In order for your personal fitness program to be successful, you must determine your needs by assessing the health-related components of fitness. The component in which you are the weakest should be given the most attention. If, for example, you need to improve your cardiovascular fitness, you should participate in activities that will elevate your pulse rate and maintain it for at least 15 to 30 minutes. Activities such as jogging, bicycling, and swimming or sports such as basketball and soccer would be appropriate selections for improving cardiovascular fitness.

You should also consider any health problems or physical impairments you may have before selecting the activities. Swimming, jogging, and bike riding are all excellent ways of improving cardiovascular fitness, but each demands something different from you. An overweight individual may not want to begin jogging because of the strain it could place on the legs and feet. For this individual, walking, swimming, or bicycling may be better choices for improving cardiovascular fitness.

Here are other health needs that must be considered in the selection of activities.

- **If you are trying to gain or lose weight, consider the caloric cost of activities.**
- **As you grow older, your interest in sports will change, the availability of other people for team sports will be less, and the amount of exercise time may decrease.**
- **If you have a physical disability, this may limit activities in which you are able to participate.**
- **A health problem may limit the degree in which you engage in vigorous activity. You should select specific activities that will help to improve your problem. For example, do exercises that will strengthen the lower back to prevent low-back pain.**

Regardless of ability or disability, all individuals must consider a number of factors in selecting activities.

SPORTS SKILLS

Your skill level will influence your success and continued participation in sports activities. Some activities require a great deal of skill. You should study the different sports activities to determine which ones are best for you, based on the level of skill you possess. Remember that an activity good for someone else may not be good for you. Try various sports activities, and evaluate them to determine if they are beneficial for you. Determine the skill requirements of the activity, such as agility, balance, power, reaction time, coordination, and speed. For example, if you are very agile and the sport selected requires a high degree of agility, you will be successful. If you experience success, you will be more likely to continue the activity and, therefore, improve your physical fitness.

STRESS DIVERSION

Stress diversion activities include those activities that can help you manage your stress. Activities that serve as stress diversion may also meet health or sports skills needs. Benefits from stress diversion activities are very personal. What may be a good stress diversion activity for you may not be good for your friends. Activities that are highly competitive are usually considered poor stress diversion activities. However, if you can participate in a competitive activity such as tennis and not be caught up in winning and losing, it could be beneficial to you in controlling your stress.

In the Sports Activities Analysis Chart, the stress diversion evaluations are based on how a majority of people respond. The chart is meant only as a guide, since stress diversion is a personal matter. In evaluating activities for stress diversion, you must consider how you respond to stress.

Coping with stress

PERSONALITY AND ATTITUDES

Your personality and attitudes are important factors that should be considered in the selection of activities for your personal fitness program. Do you prefer to exercise alone or with others? Do you prefer to compete with others or only with yourself? Do you prefer activities that are self-directed or coached? Do you prefer to exercise indoors or outdoors?

Your personality and attitudes have a bearing on the activities you select.

ALONE OR WITH OTHERS

Some people prefer to be alone with their thoughts during physical activity; some like to exercise with others. Some individuals are more successful in exercising regularly if they exercise with others. A partner, a group of friends, or family members can provide encouragement. Exercising with others may also help develop or reaffirm friendships. However, do not assume that you have to follow your friends' programs. Remember that your exercise program must be individualized to meet your needs, or you will not be satisfied.

COMPETITIVE OR NON-COMPETITIVE

Some individuals are highly competitive and prefer activities in which they compete against others. If this describes you, be careful not to let your exercise program become a contest. Exercise at your own level. Some people, on the other hand, do not like competing against others. They prefer to work on their personal fitness program alone by competing with themselves.

SELF-DIRECTED OR COACHED

Some people prefer self-directed activities. These are activities they themselves conduct, such as walking, jogging, or bicycling.

Such individuals usually possess internal motivation and enjoy competing with themselves. However, some individuals prefer activities that are conducted or coached by someone else. Such individuals tend to get psyched up by their coaches or instructors.

INDOORS OR OUTDOORS

Exercising outdoors offers variety in scenery and weather. The beauty of the outdoors motivates many people to participate in various activities such as hiking, skiing, sailing, and canoeing. Exercising indoors offers shelter from the weather and the convenience of exercising at home. Some activities, such as rope jumping, can be done indoors or outdoors. Because the activities you choose may be affected by weather, you may want to consider having an alternate. Then you can switch activities when necessary and still stay on your regular exercise schedule.

FINANCIAL CONSIDERATIONS

Much of what you need for exercise is free. Many activities require little or no equipment. For example, you can walk and jog at virtually no cost. Many communities offer free or inexpensive recreation facilities and physical activity classes. What you need to purchase will be determined by the kind of activities you include in your personal fitness program. The cost of an activity could be prohibitive, thus eliminating it from consideration.

AVAILABILITY OF FACILITIES

The availability of facilities should also be considered before selecting activities for your personal fitness program. Swimming is an excellent activity, but if a pool is not available, you need to consider something else. The same thing is true about the other components of your fitness program. Which facilities or equipment that can develop muscular strength and endurance do you have access to? You may need to rely on push-ups, sit-ups, and pull-ups, or on free weights if weight machines are not available.

Cost will have a bearing on the activities you select.

ENVIRONMENTAL CONSIDERATIONS

Often the environment is a major factor in determining the type of activity in which to participate. Weather that is either very hot and humid or very cold could influence the type of activity you plan and the time of day you do it. In highly populated areas, air pollution and personal safety are also factors that must be considered.

217

SUMMARY

The number of exercise programs and sports activities to choose from are virtually endless. An exercise program should be based on the principles of training to assure both benefit and safety. The best activities are those that you enjoy and that also meet your individual needs.

Before choosing exercise programs and sports activities for your personal fitness program, you should understand the benefits gained from each activity. Benefits vary according to the activity and the skill you possess.

In order for your personal fitness program to be successful, you must determine your physical fitness needs. Once you identify your fitness needs, specific activities can be selected for the various health-related components in need of improvement. Health problems, sports skills, stress diversion, personality and attitudes, cost, availability of facilities, and environment are also factors that affect your selection of activities. The key to developing a successful personal fitness program is designing a program that is right for you.

TRUE-FALSE

Circle "T" for all correct statements and "F" for all incorrect ones.

T F   1.   No single activity or exercise is best for everyone.

T F   2.   High-impact aerobic dance includes vigorous arm movements while keeping one foot in contact with the ground at all times.

T F   3.   Calisthenics are often used for warming up.

T F   4.   Weight training is one of the most effective exercise programs for developing muscular strength and muscular endurance.

T F   5.   Interval training can be used in swimming as well as jogging.

T F   6.   Activities that are highly competitive are usually considered poor stress diversion activities.

T F   7.   One disadvantage of swimming is the large number of injuries that occur in this activity.

T F   8.   The cardiovascular fitness benefits of swimming are considered to be high.

T F   9.   Football is an excellent activity for the development of cardiovascular fitness.

T F 10.   Pedaling a bicycle must be done continuously for at least 20 minutes in order to have an aerobic effect.

DISCUSSION

11.   What are the advantages of planned exercise programs?

12.   Why is walking a very popular form of aerobic exercise?

13.   Why should you be physically fit before participating in a sport?

14.   What are the factors you should consider when selecting activities for your personal fitness program?

15.   What is the value of exercising with a friend?

Designing Your Own Program

14

CHAPTER OBJECTIVES

As you read this chapter, look for answers to these key questions:

- What are the physical fitness components you should address when designing your personal fitness program?

- What factors should you consider when beginning a fitness program?

- What are the steps in designing a personal fitness program?

- Which motivational strategies may help you keep your program going?

VOCABULARY

After reviewing basic guidelines in initiating a personal fitness program, how would you apply the training principles and concepts in designing a program that will lead to or maintain an optimal level of:

- flexibility?
- cardiovascular fitness?
- muscular strength?
- muscular endurance?
- ideal body weight?
- stress management?

You cannot hope for success, you've got to plan for it.

DEVELOP A TOTAL PERSONAL FITNESS PROGRAM

When you hear people talk about a physical fitness program, the image that probably forms in your mind is of someone exercising informally, either running, swimming, or lifting weights. Although each of these activities is a good fitness activity, that image or picture is not a complete one. A single vigorous exercise is only one element of a total personal fitness program. Your personal program should be one that results in you looking good and feeling good. A well-rounded personal fitness program is made up of several components that require personal lifestyle choices to help you become a winner.

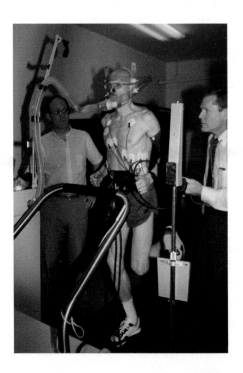

You should consider four specific areas in designing your total personal fitness program: health-related activities, sports skills, stress diversion activities, and good nutrition. Your personal fitness program should include physical activities that meet your needs in each area. Certain activities may meet your

221

Health-related activities, like bicycling or jogging, will promote fitness of the body systems.

HEY, JIM, COME ON! LET'S GO EXERCISE!

NO THANKS! I'M SORE!

Working at an intensity that creates soreness is one of the main reasons that people do not continue with a new exercise program.

needs in more than one area. For example, playing basketball not only provides you with health benefits, but it could also serve as a stress diversion activity.

STARTING YOUR PROGRAM

Many people never think about what is involved in developing a total personal fitness program. They just begin to jog with a friend or begin to lift weights. This approach usually results in an exercise program that does not develop all of the health-related components of physical fitness and may not be safe. People who begin in this manner may become sore or injured and stop exercising. Before starting your program, you should think through all the aspects and make wise decisions. At this point in the course, you should have all the information you need to make decisions about your personal fitness program.

Basic guidelines to follow when beginning a personal fitness program include (a) determining the need for a medical examination, (b) conducting a physical fitness evaluation, (c) setting realistic goals, and (d) selecting activities that help you reach those goals. Keep in mind that you have personal choices to make based on your lifestyle. Your choices should be your own, not the choices of your friends or family.

Above all, you should make sure that your personal fitness program includes all of the health-related components of physical fitness. You must decide if you want to improve each component of physical fitness, or if you want to improve only one or two components while maintaining the others. You may want to gain a few pounds, or you may want to lose a few pounds. Any personal fitness program decision you make should be based on your physical fitness assessment.

Evaluation of your current level of physical fitness is essential for a number of reasons. Once you know what your level of fitness is in each of the health-related components of physical fitness, you will be able to make good decisions, set realistic goals, design an exercise program that will bring about improvement, and use baseline data to periodically evaluate the level of improvement.

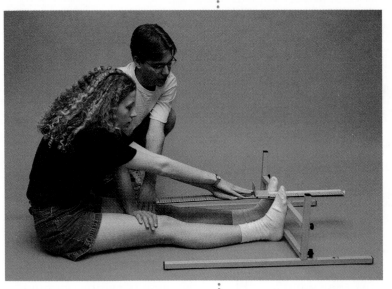

A beneficial exercise program must follow the principles of training. You should apply the principles of overload, progression, and specificity that you learned about earlier in this book. Your exercise program should be designed to overload the body system that you want to improve. It must progressively demand more of that body system and will only improve the specific part of the body that it was designed to benefit.

Assessment of your current level of physical fitness is important when planning a new program.

DESIGNING YOUR PERSONAL FITNESS PROGRAM

Now is the time to begin designing your own personal fitness program. Your current level of physical fitness should be the basis for designing your future program. Use your physical fitness test scores to establish goals. Based on your physical fitness test scores and your goals, begin designing each element of a total personal fitness program. Set realistic goals. If your physical fitness level is very low, it will take time to condition your muscles, ligaments, and other parts of your body without causing injury.

In order to design a sound personal fitness program, you should follow these specific steps.

1. Evaluation
2. Goal setting
3. Selection of activities
4. Application of training principles in designing a program
5. Periodic assessment

To help guide you in the process of designing your own program, look at the following example of a typical high school student. Study her physical fitness scores, lifestyle, realistic goals, and common-sense approach to meeting those goals.

Sports skills activities like tennis can help you develop motor skills and satisfy your need for competition, but they may also contribute to health-related fitness if your skill level allows you to play hard enough.

STEPS IN DESIGNING VANESSA'S PERSONAL FITNESS PROGRAM

Vanessa was a fifteen-year-old ninth grader who had never been very active. She spent a lot of time watching television, wishing she had the energy to learn how to play tennis and participate in some of the other activities her classmates enjoy. Even though Vanessa enjoyed swimming, she was a little overweight and felt self-conscious in a bathing suit.

EVALUATION

All students in physical education classes were given a physical fitness test during the first two weeks of school. Vanessa recorded her physical fitness test scores on the form provided: (a) cardiovascular fitness-mile run, 14:00 minutes; (b) flexibility, 18 cm; (c) sit-ups, 17; (d) pull-ups, 0; (e) body composition, 44 mm.

Health-Related Fitness Profile

NAME _Vanessa_____ AGE _15_ CLASS _2ⁿᵈ Period_____

Body Weight: _____ pounds _____ kilograms   Height: _____ feet/inches _____ meters

Fitness Components	Test Item	Test #1 Date	Health Fitness Standard	Goal	Test #2 Date
Flexibility	Sit and Reach	18 cm	25 cm	24 cm	_____
Cardiovascular	One-Mile Run	1400	1030	1030	_____
Abdominal Strength/Endurance	Sit-ups	17	34	37	_____
Upper Body Strength/Endurance	Pull-ups	0	1	1	_____
Body Composition	Skinfolds				
	1. Tricep	29	_____	_____	_____
	2. Calf	15	_____	_____	_____
	Sum of 1 & 2	44 mm	15 – 35	34	_____

GOAL SETTING

After the class had taken the first physical fitness test, Vanessa's teacher sat down with the students and talked about setting personal goals. The teacher emphasized that the students should compare their results only to themselves. This sparked an interest in Vanessa because she thought she could be successful if all she had to do was compete with herself.

With help from the teacher, Vanessa developed both short-term and long-term goals to provide direction for her personal fitness program. As the final step in goal setting, she wrote down what she thought would be the benefits of accomplishing these goals.

1. Improved appearance
2. Improved self-concept
3. Better posture
4. Improved cardiovascular endurance
5. Improved muscular endurance
6. Improved upper body strength

To keep herself motivated, Vanessa made a poster for her room listing the benefits she would obtain from her personal fitness program.

SELECTION OF ACTIVITIES

The next step for Vanessa was to decide on the activities in which she would like to participate. Using the Exercise Programs and Sports Activities Analysis Charts in Chapter 13, Vanessa compared the health-related benefits of each activity to her physical fitness goals. For example, she wanted to improve her cardiovascular fitness, so she reviewed those activities that were rated high in this component of physical fitness. Vanessa then considered her personality, attitudes, cost of activities, availability of facilities, and environmental conditions under which she would be exercising. Based on all these factors, Vanessa selected activities that would help her reach her personal fitness goals.

Evaluation of Activities

NAME Vanessa   AGE 15   CLASS Second Period

Activities	HR/SR	CV	Flex	Mus Str	Mus End	Body Com
Riding Bicycle	HR	X			some	some
Walk/Jog	HR	X			X	X
Stretching Excercise	HR		X			
Negative Pullups	HR			X	X	
Sit-ups	HR			X	X	

APPLICATION OF TRAINING PRINCIPLES IN DESIGNING A PROGRAM

Vanessa's next step was to apply the training principles to the activities she had selected. Using the information she had learned in class, Vanessa was able to personalize her program by applying the principles of overload, progression, and specificity.

CARDIOVASCULAR

Test Score: Mile Run = 14:00 minutes

Goal: To run the mile in 10 minutes, 30 seconds on the post-test

First Vanessa designed an exercise program that would help her improve cardiovascular fitness. She decided to ride her bicycle to school each day, rather than ride in the car with her father. She did not expect to ride her bicycle at a pace that would allow her heart rate to reach the lower level of her target heart rate zone of 137 beats per minute. Nor would the one-mile distance provide her sufficient time for aerobic training. However, biking the one mile to and from school each day would help improve muscular endurance in her legs and help toward her cardiovascular fitness goal.

She knew that she needed to exercise at least three days a week (frequency) at 60 to 90 percent of her maximum heart rate (intensity) for at least 20 minutes (time) to obtain all of the aerobic benefits. Vanessa decided she would walk/jog three days a week as soon as she got home from school. Her plan was to begin slowly, since she knew she was not in very good condition, based on her physical fitness test score. Therefore, in designing her program, she chose to start with a low intensity period.

Walking and jogging are excellent cardiovascular exercises.

Her goal for the first two weeks would be to walk one mile as fast as she could (intensity). After the first two weeks, she would begin to walk and jog one mile, and then continue walking until she had exercised for thirty minutes (time). She decided to jog slowly for one block, walk fast for one block, and continue alternating jogging and walking for the one mile. She would do this for at least four weeks.

After four weeks of alternating jogging and walking, Vanessa thought she would be in good enough shape to try to jog for a full mile, walk for a short distance, and then jog some more. After completing this routine, she would again continue walking fast until she had exercised for thirty minutes. By the end of three months, she hoped to be able to jog two miles at a steady pace. After she reached that level of fitness, her goal for the rest of the semester would be to continue exercising for thirty minutes, three days a week, progressively increasing her pace and the distance covered.

Cardiovascular Activity:	Bicycling	Walk/jog
(F) Number of sessions per week	10*	3
(I) Target heart rate for 10 seconds	23–31	24–28
(T) Length of session	1 mile/10 mins.	30 mins.

*Includes riding to and from school five days a week.

FLEXIBILITY

Test Score: Sit-and-Reach Test = 18 cm

Goal: To obtain a score of 24 cm on the post-test

Next Vanessa looked at flexibility. She would have to do stretching exercises, since she was not skilled at any other type of activity that could improve her flexibility. Her initial goal was to improve her fitness test score in the sit-and-reach test. Her teacher had said that they should warm up by stretching before they exercise, and repeat those same stretches in their cool-down. Vanessa decided she might as well do a warm-up, work on her flexibility and cool-down in each workout session.

Stretching exercises should be included in your exercise program not only to improve flexibility, but as part of your warm-up and cool-down to reduce the chance of injury or soreness.

She decided to add a five-minute stretching session (time) to her warm-up and cool-down for all five days (frequency) of planned exercise. She selected 10 stretching exercises and planned on holding each one for 15 seconds. Each exercise would be performed as one repetition for three sets. Her goal would be to work toward holding the stretches longer and, hopefully, be able to do 30-second stretches by the end of the semester.

Flexibility Activity:	Routine of 10 static stretches
(F) Number of sessions per week	10*
(I) Length of stretch	point of slight discomfort
(T) Time of stretch	15 sec./3 sets/per exercise
*Includes warm-up and cool-down five days a week.	

MUSCULAR STRENGTH

Test Score: Pull-ups = 0

Goal: To be able to perform 1 pull-up by the post-test.

Vanessa's teacher had told her that she should place more emphasis on muscular endurance than on muscular strength if she wanted to improve muscle tone and decrease her percentage of body fat. However, since Vanessa was unable to perform even one pull-up on the physical fitness test, she realized she had a long way to go before she could lift her body weight. Vanessa's teacher had described different exercises, including weight training, that could be used to improve her muscular strength. She was going to have to exercise at school, since she did not have any way to do pull-ups at home. She chose to use negative pull-ups to help her reach her goal of one pull-up.

Vanessa planned to work on this component of physical fitness each day at the beginning of class (frequency). She would begin by doing three negative pull-ups making each last five seconds (intensity), and trying to work up to five (time).

Muscular Strength Activity:	Negative Pull-ups
(F) Number of sessions per week	5
(I) Resistance	Body Weight/5 second count
(T) Length of session	3 to 5 repetitions

MUSCULAR ENDURANCE

Test Score: Sit-ups = 17

Goal: To be able to perform 37 by the post-test

Designing a program to help her reach her muscular endurance goal was Vanessa's next task. She knew that none of the activities she had picked would help her abdominal muscles. The best thing to do was sit-ups, even though she did not enjoy doing them. She

Negative pull-ups are another way of developing upper body strength if you cannot perform regular pull-ups. Start in a full pull-up position and slowly lower yourself, using a 5–10 second count. Make your muscles work against gravity's pull on your body weight.

decided to do one set (time) of maximum sit-ups (intensity) three nights a week (frequency) before going to bed. By the middle of the semester, she would have to reach 27 sit-ups or make an adjustment in her activity level. Her physical education teacher agreed with her assessment.

Sit-ups, like push-ups, may be modified in different ways to increase or decrease their difficulty.

Muscular Endurance Activity:	Sit-ups
(**F**) Number of sessions per week	3
(**I**) Resistance	Body weight using regular sit-ups
(**T**) Length of session	1 set of maximum sit-ups

BODY COMPOSITION

Test Score: Skin fold measurement = 44 mm

Goal: To have a body composition measurement of 34 mm by the time of the post-test

Body composition was the last component of physical fitness Vanessa had to address. Vanessa liked to eat, but she knew she had to cut down a little on her intake. She was presently consuming an average of 2,400 calories per day, or 16,800 per week. However, Vanessa's daily activity level required only 2,143 calories, or 15,000 per week. The extra 1,800 calories per week were being stored in her body as fat.

Since she had been sitting around and watching a lot of television, the exercise program that she designed would help her body composition. How could she cut calories without eliminating any of the foods she liked to eat? After reading some examples that her teacher handed out, Vanessa got an idea. Why not cut out the butter and mayonnaise that she used every day? One little pat of butter had 70 calories, and one spoonful of mayonnaise had 100 calories. Vanessa determined that she could reduce her caloric intake by 200 calories per day without giving up any real food. She liked that idea.

The personal fitness program that Vanessa designed would greatly improve her body composition. Although she occasionally engaged in physical activity, she did not burn as many calories as she took in. Using the calorie expenditure formula and the chart on Caloric Costs of Activities in Chapter 10, Vanessa calculated that she could burn an additional 272 calories per day, or approximately 1,900 calories per week. This would result in her expending 1,500 calories more than she took in.

Body Composition			
Calories Taken In		**Calories Burned**	
Present no. of calories consumed each week	16,800	Present no. of calories burned each week	−15,000
Planned calorie reduction each week	−1,400	Additional calories burned in exercise	−1,900
	15,400		−16,900
Total excess calories burned each week = 1,500 caloric reduction			

The additional calories burned each week and the planned calorie reduction would allow Vanessa to lose one-half pound of body weight per week or approximately two pounds per month. During the next sixteen weeks, Vanessa would lose eight pounds, or approximately 26 pounds in one year. One year seemed a long way off. However, Vanessa had learned in class that if she wanted to permanently lose body weight, she had to change her lifestyle and not depend on fad diets.

STRESS MANAGEMENT

Vanessa's grades were above average, and her home life was stable. She got along with her brother and sisters fairly well, and she found it easy to talk with her parents. What stress Vanessa did have was the result of her interaction with her peers. Since many of the activities she designed were stress diversion activities, she planned to use those activities for relaxation. She would also use the benefits of improved fitness to manage her stress. In addition, she identified some of her weaknesses and developed goals and a plan of action for self-improvement.

PERIODIC ASSESSMENT

Vanessa built short-term goals into her program that could be used as targets to help her periodically assess her progress toward her long-term goals. She would time herself in the mile run halfway through the semester, with her goal being 12:15. This would put her halfway to her long-term goal of being able to complete the mile run in 10:30.

In order to test her flexibility, Vanessa asked her physical education teacher if she could occasionally use the sit-and-reach box to test her progress. She decided to check her flexibility once a month. She knew her goal was slightly more than touching her

Stress diversion activities, like sailing, help individuals relax and manage stress. These activities should be a regular part of everyone's lifestyle.

toes. This information allowed her to monitor her rate of improvement without having to use the sit-and-reach box daily.

Vanessa had a long way to go before reaching her ultimate goal of being able to do one pull-up on the physical fitness test. She decided that she would try to do a regular pull-up once a week, prior to doing her sets of negative pull-ups.

Since she was going to do the maximum number she could perform, the sit-up workouts would be self-testing. She would be able to determine her progress each day.

She decided to use a combination of ways to monitor her body composition. She would weigh herself once a week, use the mirror test, ask her teacher to take her skin fold once a month, and let the fit of her clothes serve as the final judge.

Vanessa understood the importance of managing stress. She set aside thirty minutes each week to evaluate her stress level. Reflecting on the week's activities would allow her to make modifications in her stress management program.

Periodic assessment was going to be a lot of record keeping, but Vanessa thought that it could be fun and that she would be successful. Vanessa and her physical education teacher thought that the goals she had set were realistic and challenging. Her teacher also agreed that the planned personal fitness program would allow her to reach those goals. Vanessa was not sure she could reach her goals, but she was sure of one thing: she was tired of being embarrassed because she was in such poor condition. This was her program, her goals, and she was competing only against herself.

KEEP IT GOING

Starting an exercise program is not a difficult task. People do it every day. In fact, it is so easy that some individuals start a program six to ten times a year. The difficulty is continuing the program and making it a part of your lifestyle. This problem is almost always mental, seldom physical.

FIGHT BOREDOM WITH VARIETY

Boredom is possibly the biggest threat to an exercise program. You must build into your program those elements that will continue to interest you and motivate you to exercise regularly. Variety is a must. Plan for a variety of activities, a variety of people with whom you exercise, and a variety of places in which you exercise. If you only jog, you may want to jog different distances over different courses at different times of the day.

EXERCISE WITH A FRIEND

Most people are sociable individuals and like the social interaction provided by certain types of exercise. Ride your bike with people you enjoy being around. Play tennis with people whose company you enjoy. Make your self-improvement program a social activity whenever possible.

RECORD KEEPING

Record keeping and periodic evaluation can also be motivating. You should not depend on remembering the amount of the weight lifted, the number of repetitions completed, the distance covered, or the elapsed time. Writing down your performance provides you with objective measurements to help you monitor your progress. Your records will help you in setting new goals, modifying your program, and avoiding injuries. The type of information that you might want to record includes date, number of repetitions and sets, resistance, resting heart rate, exercise heart rate, distance covered, time required, weekly distance, and cumulative distance since the start of the program.

You might want to test your skills periodically against people who are better than you. Enter a road race, a tennis tournament, or a racquetball tournament. Compare the results with your previous efforts to determine how you are doing.

Make a commitment to looking good and feeling good. Make a commitment to exercising on a regular basis. Make lifestyle choices that will make you a winner.

Record keeping should be used on a regular basis to monitor progress and to serve as a motivator so that you stick with your exercise program.

Summary

A total fitness program should involve physical activities that meet personal needs in four areas: (1) health-related; (2) sports skills; (3) nutrition; and (4) stress management. When making decisions about your personal program, you must take into account a number of factors, including assessment of your present level of physical fitness. You may want to design a program for improving specific health-related components of physical fitness because your test results showed that you need only maintain other components.

You should follow five basic steps before beginning your physical fitness program: (1) evaluate your present level of physical fitness; (2) set goals; (3) select activities needed to improve your level of physical fitness; (4) design your fitness program based on the training principles; and (5) plan periodic assessment of your progress.

Start a physical fitness program and continue to make it a part of your daily routine. Fight boredom with variety. To be a winner, make a commitment to lifestyle choices that will aid you in **looking good and feeling good.**

STUDY QUESTIONS

VOCABULARY MATCHING

Place the letter of the correct answer in the space provided.

.... 1. Body composition
.... 2. Cardiovascular fitness
.... 3. Time
.... 4. Flexibility
.... 5. Health-related fitness
.... 6. Intensity
.... 7. Lifestyle choices
.... 8. Sports skills activities
.... 9. Stress diversion activities
.... 10. Total fitness

A. Activities that help people relax

B. Range of motion in your joints

C. Includes health-related components, skill-related components, and stress management

D. Concerned with the proper functioning of the body systems

E. Condition of the heart and lungs

F. How long you exercise

G. Decisions made about the way you live

H. How hard you work

I. Activities that help you develop skill

J. Ratio of fat to muscle, bone, and other tissue

TRUE-FALSE

Circle "T" for all correct statements and "F" for all incorrect ones.

T F 11. A total personal fitness program includes only vigorous activities.

T F 12. Activities that are highly competitive are good stress diversion activities.

T F 13. A fitness program can be designed to help you gain or lose weight.

T F 14. Your physical fitness program should be just like your friend's program.

T F 15. A medical exam is recommended for those over 30 years old.

T F 16. Evaluation of your physical fitness level is not important at the beginning of your program but will be important later on to determine progress.

T F 17. Goal setting is an important key to a successful personal fitness program.

T F 18. Warm-up is only important for adults who have not been exercising.

T F 19. Intensity and frequency in which exercises are performed are important aspects in designing a program.

T F 20. Boredom is the biggest threat to an exercise program.

DISCUSSION

21. What are the key decisions you should make before beginning a personal fitness program?

22. How should health-related activities, sports skill activities, and stress diversion activities be used in developing your total personal fitness program?

23. What guidelines should be used in starting a personal fitness program?

24. Identify and explain the key steps that you should go through in designing your personal fitness program.

25. What should you do to motivate yourself to continue your personal fitness program?

234

APPENDIX

APPENDIX A
ASSESSMENT STANDARDS

Health-Fitness Standards Female					
Test item					
Age	Sit-and-Reach (cm)	One-Mile Run	Sit-Ups	Pull-Ups	Sum of Skinfolds (mm)
13	25	11:00	31	1	15–35
14	25	10:30	34	1	15–35
15	25	10:30	34	1	15–35
16	25	10:30	34	1	15–35
17	25	10:30	34	1	15–35
18	25	10:30	34	1	15–35

Health-Fitness Standards Male					
Test item					
Age	Sit-and-Reach (cm)	One-Mile Run	Sit-Ups	Pull-Ups	Sum of Skinfolds (mm)
13	25	8:30	38	2	12–26
14	25	8:15	38	3	12–26
15	25	8:00	40	4	12–26
16	25	8:00	42	5	12–26
17	25	8:00	42	5	12–26
18	25	8:00	42	5	12–26

Goal Setting for Flexibility

	Distance from Health Fitness Standard		
	Less	Close	Exceeds
Difference Between Test Score and Health Fitness Standard	More than 10 cm	1 to 10 cm	At or above standard
Recommended Range for Goals	5 to 15 cm	1 to 4 cm	0 to 2 cm

Goal Setting for Cardiovascular Fitness

	Distance from Health Fitness Standard		
	Less	Close	Exceeds
Difference Between Test Score and Health Fitness Standard	2 minutes+	0 to 2 minutes	0 or better
Recommended Range for Goals	30 seconds to 90 seconds	to 5 minutes 0 to 45 seconds	15 seconds

Goal Setting for Abdominal Strength and Endurance

	Distance from Health Fitness Standard		
	Less	Close	Exceeds
Difference Between Test Score and Health Fitness Standard	More than 15	1 to 15	0 or better
Recommended Range for Goals	5 to 15	2 to 10	1 to 4

Goal Setting for Upper Body Strength

	Distance from Health Fitness Standard		
	Less	Close	Exceeds
Difference Between Test Score and Health Fitness Standard	More than 1	1–2	At or better
Recommended Range for Goals	1–3	2–5	1–3

Goal Setting for Body Composition			
	Distance from Health Fitness Standard		
	Less	Close	Exceeds
Difference Between Test Score and Health Fitness Standard	More than 10 mm	1 to 10 min	0 or better
Recommended Range for Goals	1 to 15 mm	1 to 10 mm	1 to 3 mm +/−

Summary of Flexibility Training Guidelines

Frequency At least 3 times per week.

Intensity Stretch slowly until mild tension is felt.

Time Static: Hold each stretch 15 to 30 seconds.
Dynamic: Do 10 to 20 repetitions and 1 to 3 sets.

Summary of Cardiovascular Endurance Training Guidelines

Frequency Perform at least 3 times per week.

Intensity Maintain 60 to 90% maximum heart rate.
Maintain 50 to 85% maximum heart rate reserve.

Time Maintain continuous large muscle group activity
for minimum of 20 minutes.

Summary of Muscular Fitness Training Guidelines

Muscular Endurance

Frequency Every other day for each muscle group

Intensity Low resistance (30 to 50% 1 RM)

Time High repetitions (12 to 20 reps, 1 to 3 sets)

Muscular Strength

Frequency Every other day for each muscle group

Intensity Heavy weights (60 to 90% 1 RM)

Time Low repetitions (4 to 8 reps, 1 to 3 sets)

APPENDIX D
PERCENTAGE OF
MAXIMUM HEART RATE

Percentage of Maximum Heart Rate Calculation

	Lower Limit	Upper Limit
1. Lunetta subtracted 14 (age) from 220 to obtain her maximum heart rate of 206. 220 − age = maximum heart rate.	220 − 14 = 206 MHR	220 − 14 = 206 MHR
2. She decided that 60% should be the lower limit of her target heart rate zone and that 90% would be a safe upper limit for training effect.	× 60%	× 90%
3. Lunetta multiplied Step 2 times the value of Step 1. She determined that 123.6 was the lower limit of her target heart rate zone and 185.4 was the safe upper limit.	123.6	185.4

Percentage of Maximal Heart Rate Reserve

	Lower Limit	Upper Limit
1. Chris subtracted 14 (age) from 220 to obtain his maximum heart rate of 206. 220 2 age 5 maximum heart rate.	220 − 14 = 206 MHR	220 − 14 = 206 MHR
2. Using the method described in this chapter, he determined his resting heart rate to be 70 which was subtracted from 206.	− 70 RHR = 136	− 70 RHR = 136
3. Chris decided that 50% should be the lower limit of his target heart rate zone and that 85% would be a safe upper limit for training effect	× 50%	× 85%
4. He multiplied Step 3 times the value of Step 2.	68	122.4
5. Chris then added his resting heart rate.	+ 70 RHR	+ 70 RHR
6. It was determined that 138 was the lower limit of his target heart rate zone and 186 was the safe upper limit.	138	185.6

APPENDIX E
CALORIC VALUES OF COMMON FOODS

Number of Servings Daily to Meet Individual Needs

	Women & some older adults	Children, teenage girls, active women, most men	Teenage boys & active men
Calorie level*	about 1,600	about 2,200	about 2,800
Bread group	6	9	11
Vegetable group	3	4	5
Fruit group	2	3	4
Milk group	**2–3	**2–3	**2–3
Meat group	2, for a total of 5 ounces	2, for a total of 6 ounces	3, for a total of 7 ounces

*These are the calorie levels if you choose low fat, lean foods from the five major food groups and use foods from the fats, oils, and sweets group sparingly.

**Women who are pregnant or breast feeding, teenagers, and young adults to age 24 need 3 servings.

Source: USDA

Serving Size and Caloric Values of Common Foods

Bread, Cereals, Rice, and Pasta Group	Serving Size	Calories
Bagel	1 (3″)	165
Biscuit	1 (2″)	100
Bread:		
White	1 slice	70
Whole Wheat	1 slice	65
Italian	1 slice	85
Corn	1 2½″ square	160
Cereal, dry (varies with type, check label)	1 cup	90
Cooked Grain Products		
Oatmeal	½ cup	65
Grits	½ cup	65
Spaghetti	½ cup	80
Macaroni	½ cup	80
Egg Noodles	½ cup	100
Rice	½ cup	110
Crackers:		
Saltines	4	50
Graham	2 squares	55
Hush Puppies	3	150
Muffin:		
Blueberry	1 medium	110
Bran	1 medium	105
Corn	1 medium	125

Bread, Cereals, Rice, and Pasta Group	Serving Size	Calories
Pancake	1 (4″)	60
Popcorn, popped with oil	1 cup	40
Roll:		
Hamburger/Hot Dog (1)	1	120
Submarine	1 large	390
Brown 'n Serve	1	85
Waffle	1 (7″)	210

Vegetable Group	Serving Size	Calories
Beans:		
Lima	½ cup	85
Pinto	½ cup	105
Green	½ cup	15
Broccoli	½ cup	20
Cabbage	½ cup	10
Carrots:		
Raw	1 large	40
Canned	½ cup	25
Cauliflower	½ cup	15
Cole Slaw	½ cup	85
Corn	4″ ear	100
	½ cup	70
Greens:		
Collard	½ cup	30

Vegetable Group	Serving Size	Calories
Spinach, mustard, turnip	½ cup	20
Lettuce	1 cup	5
Mixed vegetables	½ cup	60
Peas:		
Green	½ cup	75
Blackeyed	½ cup	100
Potatoes:		
Baked, no skin	1 large	140
Boiled, no skin	1 medium	70
French fries	10	110
Hash Brown	½ cup	230
Sweet:		
Baked	1 medium	160
Candied	½ medium	145
Squash:		
Summer	½ cup	15
Winter	½ cup	50
Tomato, raw	1 medium	25
Turnip	½ cup	15

Fruit Group	Serving Size	Calories
(Unless otherwise noted, values are for raw fruits and cooked vegetables)		
Apple	1 medium	85
Banana	1 medium	125
Grapefruit	½ medium	40
Grapes	10	35
Juices:		
Apple	8 oz.	120
Grape	8 oz.	165
Grapefruit	8 oz.	100
Lemon	1 Tbsp.	4
Orange	8 oz.	110
Orange	1 medium	65
Peach:		
Fresh	1 medium	40
Canned, heavy syrup	2 halves	80
Pear:		
Fresh	1 medium	100
Canned, heavy syrup	2 halves	75
Plum	1 small	30
Strawberries	½ cup	42
Watermelon	4″ × 8″ piece	110

Milk, Yogurt, and Cheese Group	Serving Size	Calories
Cheese:		
Cheddar	2 oz.	230
Swiss	2 oz.	210
Mozzarella, part skim	2 oz.	160
Cream	2 oz.	200
Cottage, 4% fat	1 cup	200

Milk, Yogurt, and Cheese Group	Serving Size	Calories
Cheese Pizza:		
Thin crust	¼ 13″ pie	340
Thick crust	¼ 13″ pie	390
Ice Cream, vanilla		
Hard	1 cup	270
Soft	1 cup	375
Milk:		
Whole	8 oz.	150
2% lowfat	8 oz.	120
2% chocolate	8 oz.	180
Skim	8 oz.	90
Buttermilk	8 oz.	90
Thick Shake:		
Vanilla	10 oz.	350
Chocolate	10 oz.	355
Yogurt:		
Plain:	8 oz.	150
Vanilla, lemon	8 oz.	200
Fruit	8 oz.	260

Meat, Poultry, Fish, Dry Beans, Eggs, and Nuts Group	Serving Size	Calories
(These figures are for meat without bone)		
Bologna	2 slices	170
Chicken:		
Breast:		
Fried	½ breast	230
Broiled, no skin	3½ oz.	165
Drumstick, fried	2 small	125
Chili con carne, with beans	1 cup	340
Chuck Roast:		
With fat	3 oz.	365
Visible fat removed	3 oz.	210
Eggs:		
Boiled	1 large	80
Scrambled	1 large	110
Fish Sticks	3 oz.	150
Ham:		
With fat	3 oz.	315
Visible fat removed	3 oz.	185
Hamburger:		
21% fat	3 oz.	245
10% fat	3 oz.	185
Hot Dog	1 (2 oz.)	150
Macaroni and cheese:		
Home recipe	1 cup	430
Canned	1 cup	230
Peanut Butter	2 Tbsp.	380
Pork Chop:		
With fat	3 oz.	310
Visible fat removed	3 oz.	215

Serving Size and Caloric Values of Common Foods — *continued*

Meat, Poultry, Fish, Dry Beans, Eggs, and Nuts Group	Serving Size	Calories
Round Steak:		
With fat	3 oz.	375
Visible fat removed	3 oz.	205
Sausage	2 small	140
Spaghetti and meat sauce	1 cup	295
Tuna Salad	½ cup	175
Turkey, light meat	3 oz.	150

Fats, Oils, and Sweets Group	Serving Size	Calories
Bacon	2 slices	85
Beer:		
Regular	12 oz.	150
Light	12 oz.	100
Butter or margarine	1 Tbsp.	100
Cake:		
Angle Food, 10"	1/12 cake	160
Chocolate with icing	1/16 cake	275
Yellow with icing	1/16 cake	275
Candy:		
Chocolate	1 oz.	145
Caramel	1 oz.	115
Hershey Bar	1½ oz.	220
Snickers	2 oz.	270
Peanut M&M's	1.7 oz.	240
Peanut Butter Cups	2 large	260
Chocolate Syrup	1 Tbsp.	45
Coca Cola	12 oz.	145
Cookies:		
Chocolate Chip	1 (2¼")	50
Oatmeal Raisin	1 (2½")	60
Oreo	1 (1¾")	60
Fig Newton	1	50
Brownie	1 (1¾")	95
Granola Bar	1	120
Doughnut:		
Cake	1	100
Glazed	1	205
Ginger Ale	12 oz.	135
Gin, Rum, Vodka, Whiskey	1½ oz.	125
Hawaiian Punch	8 oz.	120

Fats, Oils, and Sweets Group	Serving Size	Calories
Honey	1 Tbsp.	60
Ice Cream Sandwich or bar	1	165
Jam	1 Tbsp.	55
Kool Aid	8 oz.	100
Lemonade	8 oz.	110
Mayonnaise	1 Tbsp.	100
Nuts:		
Peanuts, roasted	¼ cup	340
Cashews	¼ cup	280
Pecans	¼ cup	205
Oil	1 Tbsp.	125
Pie:		
Apple	⅛ pie	300
Cherry	⅛ pie	310
Lemon Meringue	⅛ pie	270
Pecan	⅛ pie	430
Pumpkin	⅛ pie	240
Potato Chips	10	115
Pretzels, twisted	10	235
Pudding:		
Chocolate	1 cup	385
Vanilla	1 cup	285
Salad Dressing:		
Blue Cheese	1 Tbsp.	60
Italian	1 Tbsp.	70
Thousand Island	1 Tbsp.	80
Sour Cream	1 Tbsp.	25
Sprite	12 oz.	145
Sugar	1 Tbsp.	45
Tang	8 oz.	135
Tartar Sauce	1 Tbsp.	75
Tom Collins	10 oz.	180
Wine:		
Sweet	3½ oz.	135
Dry		85

From Take Control: Manage Your Weight to Look Good and Feel Great. Published by Nutrition Education and Training Program. N.C. State Dept. of Public Instruction, Healthful Living Section, Raleigh, N.C.

Caloric Values of Fast Foods*

Arby's	Calories
Beef and Cheese Sandwich	450
Club Sandwich	560
Ham 'n Cheese Sandwich	380
Junior Roast Beef Sandwich	220
Roast Beef Sandwich	350
Super Roast Beef Sandwich	620
Turkey Deluxe Sandwich	510
Turkey Sandwich	410

Burger Chef	Calories
Big Chef	542
Cheeseburger	304
Double Cheeseburger	434
Hamburger	258
Mariner Platter	680
Rancher Platter	640
Shake, Vanilla	326
Skipper's Treat	604

Burger King	Calories
Cheeseburger	305
French Fries	214
Hamburger	252
Hot Dog	291
Shake, Vanilla	332
Whaler	486
Whopper	606

Dairy Queen	Calories
Banana Split	540
Big Brazier, deluxe	470
Big Brazier, regular	457
Big Brazier with Cheese	318
Brazier Chili Dog	330
Brazier Cheese Dog	330
Brazier Dog	273
French Fries, large	320
French Fries, regular	200
Onion Rings	300
Brazier, regular	260
Oyster Bar	390
Chocolate Dipped Cone, medium	300
Chocolate Malt, medium	600
Chocolate Sundae, medium	300
Float	330
Freeze	520
Parfait	460
Ice Cream Sandwich	140
Dilly Bar	240
Fiesta Sundae	570

Dairy Queen	Calories
Fish Sandwich	400
Fish Sandwich with Cheese	440
Hot Fudge Brownie Delight	570
Mr. Misty Float	440
Mr. Misty Freeze	500
Super Brazier Chili Dog	555
Super Brazier Dog	518
Super Brazier Dog with Cheese	593

Hardee's	Calories
Apple Turnover	282
Big Twin	447
Cheeseburger	335
Deluxe	675
Double Cheeseburger	495
Fish Sandwich	468
French Fries, large	381
French Fries, regular	239
Hamburger	305
Hot Dog	346
Milkshake	391
Roast Beef Sandwich	390

Kentucky Fried Chicken	Calories
Drumstick	136
Breast	283
Rib	241
Thigh	276
Wing	151
9 Pieces Chicken	1892
Chicken Dinner, original	830
Chicken Dinner, extra crispy	950

McDonald's	Calories
Apple Pie	300
Big Mac	541
Cheeseburger	306
Cherry Pie	298
Chocolate Shake	324
Egg McMuffin	352
English Muffin, buttered	186
Fillet O'Fish	211
Hamburger	257
Hot Cakes, with butter & syrup	472
Cookies	294
Quarter Pounder with Cheese	518
Sausage	184
Scrambled Eggs	162
Strawberry Shake	345
Vanilla Shake	323

Caloric Values of Fast Foods* — *continued*

Other Mexican Foods	Calories
Enchilada:	
Beef, one	260
Beef, topped with cheese, one	340
Cheese, one	280
Guacamole, ½ cup	140
Refried Beans, ½ cup	150
Taco Salad, 1 serving	234
Tamales, one	115
Tortillas, one	40

Wendy's	Calories
Cheeseburger:	
Single with Cheese	580
Double with Cheese	800
Triple with Cheese	1040
Chili	230
French Fries	330
Frosty	390
Hamburger:	
Single	470
Double	670
Triple	850

Pizza Hut	Calories	
	Thin	Thick
Standard Cheese	180	208
Standard Pepperoni	202	224

Pizza Hut	Calories	
	Thin	Thick
Standard Pork/Mushroom	196	227
Super Supreme	266	300
Superstyle Cheese	213	235
Superstyle Pepperoni	233	244
Superstyle Pork/Mushroom	230	244
Supreme	216	244

Steak House	Entree	Dinner
Baked Potato	145	
Chopped Beef	324	727
Double Deluxe	362	791
Extra-Cut Prime Rib	409	812
Extra-Cut Ribeye	358	761
Fillet of Sole Dinner	251	654
Fillet of Sole Sandwich	122	551
French Fries	230	
Junior Patty	98	446
Prime Rib	286	689
Rib Eye/Shrimp	398	801
Shrimp	220	623
Steakhouse Deluxe	181	611
Strip Sirloin	277	680
Super Sirloin	383	786
T-Bone	374	777
Tartar Sauce, 1 Tbs.	95	

*Values are for a standard single serving size.

BIBLIOGRAPHY

Allsen, P. E.; J. M. Harrison; and B. Vance. *Fitness For Life: An Individualized Approach.* Dubuque, Iowa: William C. Brown Publishers, 1993.

Alter, Michael J. *Sport Stretch.* Champaign, Ill.: Leisure Press, 1990.

American College of Sports Medicine. "The Recommended Quantity and Quality of Exercise for Developing and Maintaining Cardiorespiratory and Muscular Fitness in Healthy Adults." *Medicine and Science in Sports and Exercise* 22 (1990):265–274.

American College of Sports Medicine. *Guidelines for Exercise Testing.* Philadelphia: Lea and Febiger, 1991.

American Heart Association. *Heart and Stroke Facts.* Dallas: The American Heart Association, 1994.

Ardell, D. B., and M. J. Tager. *Planning For Wellness.* Dubuque, Iowa: Kendall/Hunt Publishing Company, 1989.

Bailey, C. *The New Fit or Fat.* Boston: Houghton Mifflin, 1991.

Branner, T. T. *The Safe Exercise Handbook.* Dubuque, Iowa: Kendall/Hunt Publishing Company, 1998.

Coleman, E. L. *Eating for Endurance.* Palo Alto, Calif.: Bull Publishing, 1992.

Cundiff, D. E., and P. Brynteson. *Health Fitness: Guide To A Lifestyle.* Dubuque, Iowa: Kendall/Hunt Publishing Company, 1987.

De Lorme, R., and F. Stransky. *Fitness and Fallacies.* Dubuque, Iowa: Kendall/Hunt Publishing Company, 1990.

De Vries, H. A., and T. Houch. *Physiology of Exercise.* Dubuque, Iowa: Brown and Benchmark, 1994.

Fleck, S. J., and W. J. Kraemer. *Designing Resistance Training Programs.* Champaign, Ill.: Human Kinetics, 1987.

Fox, E. L.; R. W. Bowers; and M. L. Foss. *The Physiological Basis for Exercise and Sport.* Philadelphia: Saunders College Publishing, 1993.

Girandola, R. N. *Running for Lifelong Fitness.* Englewood Cliffs, N.J.: Prentice-Hall Publishing Company, 1987.

Greenberg, J. S.; G. B. Dintiman; and B. M. Oakes. *Physical Fitness and Wellness.* Englewood Cliffs, N.J.: Prentice-Hall, Inc., 1995.

Hockey, R. V. *Physical Fitness, The Pathway To Healthful Living.* St. Louis, Mo.: Times Mirror/Mosby College Publishing, 1989.

Hoeger, W. *Lifetime Physical Fitness and Wellness.* Englewood, Colo.: Morton Publishing Company, 1989.

Jackson, A. S., and M. L. Pollock. "Practical Assessment of Body Composition." *The Physician and Sports Medicine* 13 (1985):76–90.

Kraemer, William J., and J. F. Steven. *Strength Training for Young Athletes.* Champaign, Ill.: Human Kinetics Publishers, Inc., 1993.

McArdele, W. D.; F. I. Katch; and V. L. Katch. *Exercise Physiology: Energy, Nutrition, and Human Performance.* Philadelphia: Lea and Febiger, 1986.

Melograno, V. J., and J. E. Klinzing. *An Orientation to Total Fitness.* Dubuque, Iowa: Kendall/Hunt Publishing Company, 1993.

National Research Council. *Recommended Dietary Allowances.* 10th ed. Washington, D.C.: National Academy of Sciences, 1989.

Prevention Magazine. *The Prevention Index 1993: A Report Card on the Nation's Health.* Emmarus, Pa.: Prevention Magazine, 1993.

Pollock, M., and J. Wilmore. *Exercise In Health and Disease.* Philadelphia: W. B. Saunders, 1990.

Powers, S., and E. Howley. *Exercise Physiology: Theory and Application to Fitness and Performance.* 2nd ed. Dubuque, Iowa: Brown and Benchmark, 1994.

Roberts, J. A. "Exercise-Induced Asthma in Athletes." *Sports Medicine* 6 (1988):193–196.

Schroeder, Richard. *Assessing Fitness: Your Guide to a Healthy Lifestyle.* Dubuque, Iowa: Kendall/Hunt Publishing Company, 1990.

Senate Select Committee on Nutrition and Human Needs. *Dietary Goals for the United States.* 2nd ed. Washington, D.C.: U.S. Senate Select Committee, 1986.

Smart Moves. Dairy and Food Nutrition Council of Florida. Orlando, 1990.

Thygerson, A. L. *Fitness and Health: Lifestyle Strategies.* Boston: Jones and Bartlett, 1989.

U.S. Department of Health and Human Services. Healthy People 2000 Objectives and The National Education Goals. *Public Health Reports* 107 no. 1 (1992):9–14.

U.S. Department of Health and Human Services. *The Surgeon General's Report on Nutrition and Health.* DHHS (PHS) Publication No. 88-50211. Washington, D.C.: U.S. Government Printing Office, 1998.

Williams, M. *Lifetime Fitness and Wellness.* Dubuque, Iowa: William C. Brown, 1996.

GLOSSARY

A

abdominals — group of muscles forming the supporting wall of the abdominal region

acclimatization — the process of the body slowly adapting to a new temperature

achilles tendon — tendon connecting the calf muscle to the heel of the foot

adipose tissue — fat tissue

adrenaline — chemical secreted by the adrenal glands which moves the body into the fight or flight response

advertising — describing or presenting a product in order to induce people to buy, support, or approve it

aerobic — *with oxygen;* term refers to energy-producing biochemical pathways in cells that use oxygen to produce energy

agility — the ability to change the position and control the movement of the whole body

alarm stage — first stage of stress where the stressor is identified and adrenaline is released

alveoli — small air sacs in the lungs where exchange of air into the blood takes place

anabolic steroids — a synthetic version of the male sex hormone, testosterone

anaerobic — *without oxygen;* term refers to energy producing biochemical pathways in cells that do *not* require oxygen to produce energy

anorexia nervosa — an eating disorder in which a person refuses to eat normally, resulting in extreme thinness and even starvation

aorta — large artery that carries blood away from the heart to be carried throughout the body

artery — a vessel that carries blood away from the heart

atherosclerosis — a condition in which fatty deposits build up on inner walls of arteries, causing narrowing of the arterial passageway

atrium — the top two chambers of the heart which receive blood from the veins and forces it into the lower two chambers of the heart

atrophy — the wasting away or decrease in size of a body part, particularly muscle

balance — ability to keep an upright posture while either standing still or moving

ballistic stretching — stretching that involves bobbing, bouncing or jerky movements that make use of the body's momentum

basal metabolism — the amount of energy required to maintain the body at rest

behavior modification — the technique used to promote desirable changes in behavior

blood pressure — the measure of blood force against the walls of the arteries

body composition — the ratio of fat to muscle, bone, and other body tissues

body image — the way one sees oneself physically

bulimia — an eating disorder characterized by overeating followed by self-induced vomiting, use of laxatives, or very strenuous exercise to avoid weight gain

calisthenics — exercises in which body weight is used as the resistance

calorie — the amount of energy needed to raise the temperature of one kilogram of water one degree centigrade; a unit that measures the energy in foods

concentric contraction — the shortening of a muscle due to contraction; also called positive work

capillary — a network of small vessels located between the arteries and veins in which exchanges of vital substances occur between tissue and blood

carbohydrates — the essential nutrients that are the body's primary source of energy

cardiovascular fitness — the ability of the heart, blood vessels, and respiratory system to supply oxygen and nutrients to the muscles during exercise

carotid artery — a major artery (or pair of arteries) located on each side of the neck allowing blood to flow from the aorta to the head

cholesterol — a waxy, fatlike substance found in animal tissue

circuit training — an exercise program in which one moves around a prescribed course, stopping at each station to perform a specified exercise

circulatory system — the system consisting primarily of the blood, heart, and blood vessels

consumer — a person who buys goods and services

cool-down — a 10- to 15-minute period of mild exercise following vigorous exercise that allows the body and heart rate to return to normal

coordination — the integration of eye, hand, and foot movements

creeping obesity — the gaining of fat slowly over a period of time

criterion-referenced tests — physical fitness tests in which specific standards are used to judge fitness levels

cross-train — to engage in a variety of activities and exercises from day to day

dehydration — the loss of water from body tissues

diabetes — the body's inability to regulate sugar metabolsim

diaphragm — a large muscle in the upper abdomen

diastolic blood pressure — the blood pressure exerted during the relaxation phase of the heart cycle

distress — negative stress resulting from difficulties

diuretics — the drugs used to control accumulation of fluids in body tissues, congestive heart failure, and high blood pressure

dynamic stretching — stretching done in a continuous, slow, and controlled manner

eccentric contraction — isotonic contractions in which the muscle exerts force while the muscle lengthens; also called negative work

ectomorph — a body type with a slender, slight build

edema — an accumulation of fluid in body tissues

electrical impedance — method of determining body fat by measuring electrical resistance encountered in the body

endormorph — a body type with a large, soft bulging body and pear-shaped appearance

eustress — positive stress resulting from something good

exercise prescription — a personalized amount of exercise that promotes physical fitness

F

fad diets — diets that promote weight loss without sound nutritional practices

fallacy — an idea that is the result of deception or incorrect information

fast-twitch fibers — white muscle fibers that contract quickly, allowing explosive muscular contractions

fat — an efficient storage of energy. Excess fat is stored in fat cells called adipose tissue located under the skin and around internal organs

fat-soluble vitamins — vitamins that can be stored in fat deposits in the body; i.e., vitamins A, D, E, and K

fight or flight response — an involuntary physical response to a stressor that gives an individual the capacity for sudden and quick action

F.I.T. — the three ways to achieve overload in a physical fitness program—frequency, intensity, and time

flexibility — the range of possible movement at various joints

Food Guide Pyramid — a visual guideline established by U.S. Department of Agriculture to ensure that all of the essential nutrients are included in the daily diet

fraudulent — characterized by deceit or trickery used to gain an unfair or dishonest advantage

frequency — the number of times one should exercise to improve a component of physical fitness

G

general stressors — those types of stimuli that trigger the stress response but are not easily identifiable by the body

glucose — the only sugar molecule that can be used by the body in its natural form and serves as a valuable source of energy

goal setting — a process designed to motivate people to make lifestyle changes toward self-improvement

H

HDL — *h*igh *d*ensity *l*ipoprotein that helps remove excess cholesterol

health-related fitness — components of physical fitness that contribute to the operation of the systems of the body

health-related fitness standards — satisfactory or healthy levels of flexibility, cardiovascular fitness, muscular strength and endurance, and body composition

health risk factors — those factors associated with disease, disability, and premature death

heart attack — the damage or death of heart tissue as a result of the heart not receiving a sufficient blood supply

heart rate — the number of heart beats per minute

heat cramps — a heat-related problem in which certain muscles contract involuntarily and cause pain

heat exhaustion — a condition characterized by profuse sweating, dizziness, and extreme weakness

heat stroke — a medical emergency characterized by hot, dry skin and a rising body temperature

hemoglobin — an iron-rich compound in the blood that helps carry oxygen to the muscles, tissues, and organs

high-density lipoproteins (HDL) — a type of cholesterol that is associated with lowering fatty plaque accumulation in the coronary arteries that lead to heart disease. HDL-cholesterol is often called "good cholesterol"

high-impact aerobics — aerobic dance that includes jumping, bouncing, and running

homeostasis — the internal balance of the body

humidity — the amount of water vapor in the air

hydrostatic weighing — a method of determining body composition that involves weighing a person both outside and inside a tank of water

hypertension — an unstable or persistent elevation of blood pressure above normal range, commonly called high blood pressure

hyperthermia — an increase in body temperature with a reduction of body fluids

hypothermia — an excessive decline in body temperature

ideal body weight — the amount a person weighs if he or she has an appropriate percentage of body fat

inactivity — the lack of physical activity and exercise

intensity of exercise — the degree to which one should exercise to improve fitness

intermediate fibers — muscle fibers that possess a combination of the fast and slow-twitch fiber characteristics

interval training — an exercise program that involves a series of exercises interspersed with rest periods

isokinetic exercises — exercises done with special machines that allow for maximum resistance over the complete range of motion

isometric exercises — exercises in which one contracts muscles but does not move body parts

isostatic stretching — a form of stretching in which the body is pushed beyond its initial limit

isotonic exercises — exercises in which a muscle lengthens and shortens through its full range of movement while lowering and raising a resistance

lactic acid — a waste product built up in the body as a result of severe muscular exercise

LDL — *low density lipoprotein* that leads to a buildup of cholesterol on artery walls

lean body mass — body mass made up of muscle tissue and other nonfat tissue such as bones, ligaments, and tendons

lifetime sports — individual sports that can be engaged in for a lifetime

ligament — strong, fibrous tissue that attaches one bone to another

lifestyle — daily choices you make in regards to what you eat, consume, and activities in which you engage

long-term goals — those goals that take a long time, perhaps years, to reach

low-impact aerobics — aerobic dance that includes vigorous arm movements while keeping one foot in contact with the ground at all times

M

maximum heart rate — the heart rate that should not be exceeded during exercise; calculated by subtracting one's age from 220

media — the newspapers, magazines, television, and radio

meditation — where one focuses their thoughts for the purpose of relaxation

mesomorph — a body type with a solid, muscular, and large-boned physique

metabolic rate — total calories burned or expended as heat

minerals — the essential nutrients needed by the body in small amounts to prevent deficiencies and diseases

muscle-bound — characterized by an imbalanced development of strength between the antagonist and agonist muscle in which a loss of flexibility occurs

muscle endurance — the ability to use muscles for a long period of time

muscular strength — the ability of muscles to exert a force one time

N

negative coping techniques — those responses that ease or disguise the symptoms of stress and that are harmful to an individual and those around him or her

norm-referenced tests — physical fitness tests in which norms are used to indicate fitness levels

nutrient — a substance contained in food which is necessary for good health

nutrition — the study of how the body uses the nutrients in food you eat

O

obese — having an excessive amount of body fat

obesity — a condition characterized by excessive deposits of fat on the body

one-repetition maximum (1 RM) test — a measurement of the maximum amount of weight that can be lifted one time

osteoporosis — the loss of bone mass and strength, which increases risk of bone fractures

overload principle — a basic principle of fitness training in which the body is stressed and adapts to that stress

overuse injury — an injury caused by not following the correct progression, doing an exercise too much, too soon, or too often

overweight — a condition that exceeds the desirable body weight by 10 percent, according to height and weight charts

P

percentage of heart rate reserve — a method of calculating cardiovascular exercise intensity based upon 50 to 85 percent of your maximum heart rate reserve

percentage of maximum heart rate — a method of calculating cardiovascular exercise intensity based upon 60 to 90 percent of your maximum heart rate

physical fitness — the capacity of the whole body to function at optimum efficiency; determined by the condition of the heart and circulatory, respiratory, and muscular systems, the degree of flexibility, and the percentage of body fat

planned program — a program that includes specific exercises for persons of specific fitness levels or ages

positive coping strategies — strategies designed to deal with unavoidable stress

power — ability to do strength performances at a rapid pace

principle of overload — exposing the muscles, joints, and cardiovascular and respiratory systems to more work and stress than is normally experienced

principle of progression — a progressive increase in the level of exercise in order to sustain improvement in physical fitness

principle of specificity — the performance of specific exercises in order to improve specific components of physical fitness in specific body parts

progression, principle of — principle of training that dictates that overload should be increased gradually

progressive muscle relaxation — relaxation program where muscles are relaxed group by group

proteins — the essential nutrients needed for growth and repair of body tissues

pulse — a regular throbbing caused by pressure of blood on an artery wall that corresponds to heart beat

quack — one who promotes useless and sometimes harmful practices as beneficial

quackery — the promotion of useless and sometimes harmful practices as beneficial

reaction time — the amount of time needed to move once the senses signal the need to move

Recommended Daily Allowance (RDA) — the amount of nutrients recommended daily by the U.S. Department of Agriculture

recovery heart rate — the existing heart rate just after exercise

red blood cell — the cell that carries oxygen to the tissues

rehydration — the replacement of fluids that have been lost from the body

relaxation techniques — those activities that reduce muscle tension and stress in the body through concentration of the mind

repetition — the completion of a single, full-range movement of the body part being exercised

respiratory system — the system composed of lungs and air passages that help supply oxygen to the body

resting heart rate — the existing heart rate just after waking and before getting out of bed

resting metabolic rate (RMR) — calories expended while at rest

R.I.C.E. — the letters stand for the first letters of words used in first aid for certain injuries: R = Rest; I = Ice; C = Compression; E = Elevation

risk factor — a trait that increases the likelihood one will develop chronic diseases

saturated fats — those fats contained in animal products

set — a group of repetitions performed one after the other

set point theory — the theory that body weight is controlled at a set point by a weight-regulating control center within the brain

shin splint — an inflammation of the membrane on the front of the bones in the lower leg

short-term goals — those goals that can be reached in a short period of time

skill-related fitness — the components of physical fitness that contribute to the ability to successfully participate in sports

skinfold caliper — a device used to measure a fold of skin and its underlying layer of body fat

slow-twitch fibers — red muscle fibers that are slow to contract but have the ability to continue contracting for long periods of time

somatotype — body type

specificity, principle of — principle of training that states the exercise training effect is specific to those muscles involved in the activity

speed — the ability to cover a distance in a short time

sports skills activities — those activities that help develop sports skills and satisfy the need for competition

spot reduction myth — the mistaken belief that exercising muscles in a particular area of the body will remove fat from that area

static stretching — the slow movement of a muscle to the stretching point at which it is held for 15 seconds

stitch in the side — sharp pain in the side just under the ribs

strain — damage to a ligament that occurs if excessive force is applied to a joint

stress — the nonspecific response of the body to demands made upon it

stress diversion activities — those activities, both active and passive, that reduce or divert stress

stress fracture — tiny cracks or bsreaks in bone, usually caused by overuse

stressor — a stimulus (event, situation, or activity) that causes stress

stroke — brain damage that occurs when blood supply to the brain is reduced

stroke volume — the amount of blood the heart pumps out of the left ventricle on each contraction

systolic blood pressure — the blood pressure during the contraction phase of the heart

target heart rate — 60 to 90 percent of the maximum heart rate; results in greatest cardiovascular benefits from exercise

tendon — connective tissue that anchors muscles to bones

testosterone — male hormone that helps build muscle

time — how long one exercises to improve fitness

time line — a tool used to organize and plot the course toward a major goal

unsaturated fats — those fats found in plant sources

vegetarian — one who eliminates animal products from their diet

vein — a vessel that carries blood to the heart

ventricles — the bottom two chambers of the heart

vitamin — a nutrient that helps control growth and maintain body functions

warm-up — a 10- to 15-minute light exercise period during which the body is prepared for vigorous exercise

water-soluble vitamins — those vitamins that dissolve in water and cannot be stored in body tissues

INDEX

Abdominals
    exercises for developing, 124
    goal setting for improving strength and endurance, 114–115
Achilles tendon stretch, 81
Adrenaline, 178, 180
Advertising, 193
    false, 193, 195, 200–201
    as influence on buying decisions, 193
Aerobic dance, 207
Aerobic exercise, 19–20, 91, 94, 100
Age
    and basal metabolic rate, 160
    and ideal body weight, 156
    as risk factor, 8–9
Agility, 23
Air pollution, 54
Alcohol, 187
Amino acids, 134–135
Anabolic steroids, 198–199
    definition of, 198
    effects of, 198–199
Anaerobic exercise, 100
Animal protein, 135
Ankle, sprained, 59
Anorexia nervosa, 168
Appearance, exercise as factor in improved, 9
Appetite, and physical activity, 169
Appetite suppressants, 197
Aqua dynamics, 207
Arm circles, 82
Arms, exercises for developing, 118–121
Arteries, 88
Assessment, of flexibility, 78
Atherosclerosis, 92
Athletic shoes, 49
Atrophy, 106
Attitudes
    in selecting physical activities, 216–217
    toward physical fitness, 1, 3–5
Avoidance, 179

Back
    exercises for developing, 123
    pain in lower, 75
Balance, 24
Ball-and-socket joint, 73
Ballistic stretching, 76, 77
Belief, 37
Bench press, 122
Bent-knee sit-ups, 124
Bicycling, 207
Blisters, 58
Blood, circulation of, 88–89
Blood pressure, 91
    high, 6, 180
Body
    effects of anabolic steroids on, 198
    reactions to stress, 178–180
Body circumference measurements, 158

Body composition, 22–23, 155–157
    application of training programs in, 229–230
    goal setting for, 168–169
Body fat
    excess, as unhealthy, 159
    versus lean body mass, 155
    methods of measuring, 157–158
Body image, 22
    exercise as factor in improved, 10
Body types, 153–154
Body weight
    ideal, 156–157
    as misleading, 5
Body wraps, 196
Bulimia, 168
Bust developers, 196
Buying decisions, influences on, 192–193

Calcium, 137
Calf, exercises for developing, 126
Calf skinfold measurements, 22–23
Calf stretch, 81
Calisthenics, 208
Caloric cost of physical activities, 162–165
Calorie requirements, determining daily, 146–148
Capillaries, 89
Carbohydrates, 135
    on food labels, 141–142
    starches and sugars in, 135–136
Cardiovascular disease
    causes of, 92
    risk factors for, 92–93
Cardiovascular fitness, 19–20, 86–102
    anatomy in, 88–89
    application of training principles for, 94–100, 226–227
    assessing, 20
    benefits of exercise for, 93–94
    blood pressure in, 91–92
    definition of, 88
    goal setting for, 101
    importance of, 87–88
    monitoring of heart in, 89–91
Cardiovascular heart disease, age as risk factor for, 8–9
Chest, exercises for developing, 122–123
Chest and biceps stretch, 79
Chin-ups, 21
Cholesterol, 136
    as risk factor, 7
Circuit training, 208
Circulatory system, 88–89
Clothes, fitness, 48–50
Coached activities, 216–217
Cold weather, exercise in, 52–53
Compensation, 179
Competitive activities, 216
Consumers, 190–202
    becoming knowledgeable, 194
    definition of, 191
    influences on buying decisions of, 192–193

Contributing health risk factors, 9
Cooling down, 56
    activities in, 57
    benefits of, 56–57
Coordination, 25
Creeping obesity, 160
Criterion-referenced tests, 27
Curl-ups, 124

Deep knee bends, 83
Desire, 36
Diabetes, 9
Diaphragm, 58
Diastolic pressure, 91
Diet. *See also* Nutrition
    daily, 148–149
    fad, 134, 198
Diet log, 148–149
Distance runs, 20
Distress, 180–181
Diuretics, 197
Dogs, 54
Drugs, 187
    and weight control, 197–198
Dynamic stretching, 76

Eating disorders, 168
Ectomorph body type, 154
Edema, 197
Electric stimulators, 196
Emotional tension, relieving, 75
Endomorph body type, 154
Energy, exercise as factor in improved, 11
Environment, in selecting physical activities, 217
Essential amino acids, 134–135
Estrogen, 106
Eustress, 180
Exercise facilities, availability of, 217
Exercise programs, 206–211
    analysis of, 211
    fitness evaluation in starting, 48
    goal setting in, 48
    medical exam in starting, 47–48
Exercises
    aerobic, 19–20, 91, 94, 100, 207
    anaerobic, 100
    benefits of
        better sleep, 12
        cardiovascular, 93–94
        enjoyment of life, 10
        improved appearance, 9
        improved body image, 10
        improved health, 10
        improved physical performance, 11–12
        improved self-control, 10
        increased energy, 11
        increased life expectancy, 13
        increased muscular strength and endurance, 11, 117–127
        increased success, 12
        stress management, 12
    clothes for, 48–50
    in cold weather, 52–53
    and fat loss, 168
    and flexibility, 78–82
    gadgets and gimmicks for, 196
    in hot weather, 50–51
    isokinetic, 109–110

isometric, 108–109
isotonic, 109
safety precautions for, 53–54

Fad, 2
Fad diets, 134, 198
False advertising, 195, 200–201
Fast-twitch fibers, 107, 111
Fat cell growth, vulnerable stages for, 159–160
Fat loss, and exercise, 168
Fats, 136–137
    in Food Guide Pyramid, 144–145
    on food labels, 141–142
Fat-soluble vitamins, 138
Federal Trade Commission, 201
Fiber, 136
Fight or flight response, 178–179
Finance in selecting physical activities, 217
Fitness. *See* Personal fitness; Physical fitness
Fitness centers, 199–200
Fitness evaluation, 48
Fitness trails, 208
Flexed-arm hang, 21
Flexibility, 18–19, 72–84
    application of training principles to, 76–77, 227–228
    assessment of, 78
    definition of, 73–74
    exercises for, 78–82
    goal setting for improving, 78
    importance of, 74–75
    safety precautions for, 77–78
    and stretching, 75–76, 82–83
Flies, 122
Food. *See also* Nutrition
    acquired experiences with, 132–133
    historical use of, 132
    relation to health, 133
Food and Drug Administration, 201
Food Guide Pyramid, 142–146
    fats in, 144–145
    food groups in, 145–146
    sugars in, 144–145
Food labels, 139–142
Four-count toe touch, 83
French curl, 120
Frequency/intensity/time (FIT), 65–66
    and cardiovascular fitness, 99–100
    and flexibility, 76–77
    and muscular fitness, 111–113
Frequency of exercise, 95
    for cardiovascular fitness, 95
    and muscular fitness, 111
Front curl, 119
Frostbite, 52

General adaptation syndrome, 178
Glucose, 135
Goals
    definition of, 35
    long-term, 35
    short-term, 36
Goal setting, 29, 35–36
    for abdominal strength and endurance, 114–115
    in action, 40–43
    for body composition, 168–169
    for cardiovascular fitness, 101
    in developing personal fitness program, 225

to improve flexibility, 78
realistic, 37
in starting exercise program, 48
steps in, 36–40
in stress management, 183–184
for upper body strength, 115
Granular problems and obesity, 169
Groin stretch, 81

Habit as influence on buying decisions, 193
Half-knee bends, 125
Hamstring curl, 126
Hamstring stretch, 80
HDL, 136–137
Head circles, 82
Health
exercise as factor in improved, 10
needs in selecting physical activities, 214
relation of food to, 133
taking control of, 34–35
Health claims and nutrition, 141
Health clubs, 199–200
Health-related fitness, 17, 18–23
standards for, 27–28
Health risk factors
contributing, 9
primary, 6–9
Heart, 88. *See also* Cardiovascular disease; Cardiovascular
fitness
monitoring, 89–91
Heart rate, 89
maximum, 96
recovery, 91
resting, 90
target, 96, 98
Heat cramps, 50
Heat exhaustion, 51
Heat illness, 50–51
preventive measures for, 51–52
Heat stroke, 51
Heel raiser, 126
Height and weight charts, 155
Heredity
and physical fitness, 4
as risk factor, 8
High blood pressure, 180
as risk factor, 6
High-impact aerobics, 207
Hinge joints, 73
Homeostasis, 176
Hot weather, exercise in, 50–51
Hurdle stretch, 83
Hyperthermia, 50
Hypothermia, 52

Ideal body weight, 156–157
Illness
cardiovascular, 92–93
heat, 50–52
Inactivity as risk factor, 6, 94
Indoor activities, 217
Injuries, 57–59
reducing, 75
Intensity
for cardiovascular fitness, 95–98
of exercise, 66
and muscular fitness, 111–112

Intermediate-twitch fibers, 107
Interval training, 208–209
Iodine, 137
Iron, 137
Isokinetic exercises, 109–110
Isometric exercises, 108–109
Isostatic stretching, 76
Isotonic exercises, 109

Jogging, 209
Joint, 73
ball-and-socket, 73
hinge, 73
pivot, 73
range of motion for, 74

Kneeling knee tuck, 123
Knee push-ups, 118

Labels, food, 139–142
LDL, 136–137
Lean body mass, 155
Leg extension, 125
Life, exercise as factor in more enjoyment of, 10
Life expectancy, exercise as factor in improved, 13
Lifestyle and nutrition, 133
Lifetime sports, 212
Ligaments, 74
Long-term goals, 35
Lower back stretch, 80
Low-impact aerobics, 207

Massage, 196
Maximum heart rate, 96
Media. *See also* Advertising
influence on physical fitness, 5
Medical exam, 47–48
Mesomorph body type, 154
Metabolism, basal, 146, 160
Milo of Crotona, 64, 67
Mind, reaction to stress, 179–180
Minerals, 137
Motorized exercise devices, 196
Muscle fiber, composition of, 107
Muscles, 74
and anabolic steroids, 198–199
atrophy of, 106
Muscle soreness, 57–58
Muscular endurance, 20–21, 105–106, 113
application of training programs in, 228–229
exercise as factor in improved, 11
Muscular fitness, 104–128
application of training principles to, 110–114
exercises for improving, 117–127
goal setting for, 114–115
methods of developing, 108–110
Muscular strength, 20–21, 105–106, 113
application of training programs in, 228
exercise as factor in improved, 11

Neck stretch, 79
Negative coping techniques, 185–187
Negative pull-ups, 119
Negative stress, 180–181
effects of, 181
Non-competitive activities, 216
Non-meat protein, 135

Norm-referenced tests, 27
Nutrition, 130–150
    and acquired experiences with food, 132–133
    benefits of, 149
    carbohydrates in, 135–136
    and daily diet, 148–149
    determining daily calorie requirements, 146–148
    fiber in, 136–137
    and Food Guide Pyramid, 142–146
    food labels in, 139–142
    and historical use of food, 132
    minerals in, 137
    proteins in, 134–135
    relation of food to health, 133–134
    and stress management, 182
    vitamins in, 138–139
    water in, 139

Obesity, 156
    creeping, 160
    as risk factor, 6
One-arm raising, 122–123
Outdoor activities, 217
Overload, principle of, 64, 76, 95, 111
    for cardiovascular fitness, 95
    and flexibility, 76
    and muscular fitness, 111
Overweight, 156

Parallel bar dips, 21
Peers, influence of, 192–193
Percentage of maximal heart rate reserve, 98
Percentage of maximum heart rate calculation, 97–98
Periodic self-testing, 26–27
Personal fitness, 1
    developing total program for, 221–232
        application of training principles in designing, 226–230
        evaluation in, 224, 230–231
        goal setting in, 225
        selection of activities for, 225
    keeping program going, 231–232
    as personal matter, 64
    record keeping for, 232
    taking control of, 34–35
Personality in selecting physical activities, 216–217
Personal safety, 54
Phosphorus, 137
Physical activities
    caloric cost of, 162–165
    categories of, 206–213
    considerations in selecting, 214–217
    selection of, for personal fitness program, 225
    Surgeon General's Report on, 3
    valuation of, 204–218
Physical fitness
    analyzing, 17
    assessment of, 26–27
        interpreting results, 27–28
    attitude toward, 1, 3–5
    definition of, 5–6
    health-related, 17, 18–23
    skill-related, 17, 23–26
    and stress management, 182
    as trend, 2–3
Physical performance, exercise as factor in improved, 11–12
Pivot joints, 73
Planned programs, 206

Plow, 82
Positive coping strategies, 182–183
Positive stress, 180
Post-exercise pain, preventing, 75
Posture, 105–106
Potassium, 137
Power, 24–25
Preventive measures for heat illness, 51–52
Primary health risk factors, 6–9
Progression, principle of, 67–68
    and cardiovascular fitness, 100
    and flexibility, 77
    and muscular fitness, 113–114
Projecting, 179
Proteins, 134
    animal, 135
    composition of, 134–135
    on food labels, 141–142
    non-meat, 135
Pull-ups, 21, 119
Pull-up test, 22
Pulse, 90, 95
Push-ups, 21, 118

Quadriceps stretch, 81
    sitting, 82

Rationalizing, 179
Reaction time, 25
Record keeping, 232
Recovery heart rate, 91
Repetition, 112
Resistance, 111
Resistance training, 114
Respiratory system, 88–89
Resting heart rate, 90
Reverse curl, 119
Reverse wrist curl, 121
Risk factors for cardiovascular disease, 92–93
Rope jumping, 209
Rubberized suits, 196

Safety precautions, 53–54
    and flexibility, 77–78
Saturated fats, 136
Sauna baths, 196
Sauna suits, 196
Self-control, exercise as factor in improved, 10
Self-directed activities, 216–217
Set, 112
Sex of individual
    and ideal body weight, 156
    as risk factor, 8
Shin stretch, 82
Shirts, 50
Shoes, 49
Shorts, 50
Short-term goals, 36
Shoulders, exercises for developing, 117–118
Shoulder shrug, 117
Shoulder stretch, 80
Side leg lifts, 124
Sitting quadriceps stretch, 82
sit-ups, 124
Sit-up test, 21
Skill-related fitness, 17, 23–26
Skinfold calipers, 22–23, 158

Skinfold measurements, 158
Skin splints, 58
Sleep, exercise as factor in improved, 12
Slow-twitch fibers, 107, 111
Smoking, as risk factor, 7–8
Socks, 49
Sodium, 137
Somatotype, 153
Specificity, principle of, 68
   and cardiovascular fitness, 100
   and flexibility, 77
   and muscular fitness, 114
Speed, 26
Sports skills, 212
   analysis of, 212–213
   in selecting physical activities, 215
Spot reduction, 169, 194–195
Sprained ankle, 59
Standing lateral raise, 117
Standing long jump, 25
Starches, 135–136
Static stretching, 75–76
Step tests, 20
Steroids. *See* Anabolic steroids
Stimulus, 178
Stitch in the side, 58–59
Stress, 172–188
   causes of, 176–178
   definition of, 175–176
   effects of, 180–181
   exercise as factor in coping with, 12
   importance of understanding, 176
   individual reactions to, 176, 178–180
   negative, 180–181
      effects of, 181
   positive, 180
   recognizing early symptoms of, 182
   as risk factor, 7
Stress diversion
   activities in, 184–185
   in selecting physical activities, 215
Stressful situations, identifying, 182–183
Stress management
   application of training programs in, 230
   developing program for, 181–184
   goal setting in, 183–184
   negative coping techniques to avoid, 185–187
Stressors, 176
   forms of, 177–178
   identifying, 177
Stretching
   harmful positions in, 82–83
   types of, 75–76
Success, exercise as factor in improved, 12
Sugars, 135–136
   in Food Guide Pyramid, 144–145
Support groups, in stress management, 183
Surgeon General's Report on physical activity, 3
Sweating, 50
Swimming, 210, 217
Systolic pressure, 91

Target heart rate, 96, 98
Tendons, 74
Tension as risk factor, 7
Testimonials, 200

Testosterone, 21, 106
Thighs, exercises for developing, 124–126
Three-prong support side stretch, 80
Thyroid hormones, 197
Time
   for cardiovascular fitness, 99–100
   of exercise, 66
   and muscular fitness, 112–113
Time line, 39
Time management, 184
Training, efficient and safe, 63
Training principles, 62–69
   for cardiovascular fitness, 94–100
   for muscular fitness, 110–114
   in personal fitness program, 226–230
Training programs
   frequency in, 65, 95, 111
   intensity in, 66, 95–98, 111–112
   overload principle in, 64, 76, 95, 111
   progression principle in, 67–68, 77, 100, 113–114
   specificity principle in, 68, 77, 100, 114
   time in, 66, 99–100, 112–113
Trend, 2
Triceps press, 120
Triceps skinfold measurements, 22–23
Triceps stretch, 79
Two-arm press, 120

Underwater weighing, 22, 157
Unsaturated fats, 136
Upper back lift, 123
Upper body and torso stretch, 79
Upper body strength, goal setting for, 115
Upright rowing, 118

Veins, 89
Ventricle, 88
Vertical jump, 25
Vibrating belts, 196
Vitamins, 138
   balanced approach to, 139
   consumer concerns regarding, 139
   fat-soluble, 138
   water-soluble, 138–139

Walking, 210
Warming up, 55
   activities in, 56
   benefits of, 55–56
Water, 139
Water-soluble vitamins, 138–139
Weight control
   and drugs, 197–198
   importance of, 159–160
   misconceptions on, 168
   permanent methods of, 165–167
   and spot reduction, 194–195
Weight gain, 161–162
Weight loss, 161
Weight maintenance, 162
Weight training, 116–117, 210
   myths about, 106
Wrist curls, 121

Youth sports, past experience with, 4

PHOTO CREDITS

Cover | **2 Runners, Weight Lifter** Kendall/Hunt Publishing by Ron Franklin

Chapter 1 | **Cheerleaders** Kendall/Hunt Publishing by Ron Franklin

Chapter 2 | **Sit and Reach, 5 Runners, Sit-ups, Pull-ups, Triceps Skinfold, Calk Skinfold, One Foot Balance, Balance Beam, Vertical Jump, Reaction Time** Kendall/Hunt Publishing by Ron Franklin
Downhill Skier From John Weiland/National Sports Center for the Disabled. Printed with permission.

Chapter 3 | **Recording Progress, Taking Pulse, Joggers** Kendall/Hunt Publishing by Ron Franklin
Blind Snowshoer From Darcy Kiefel/National Sports Center for the Disabled. Printed with permission.

Chapter 4 | **Screened photo, Ankle Wrap, Silhouette, Buying Shoes, Drinking Water** Kendall/Hunt Publishing by Ron Franklin

Chapter 5 | **Bench Press, 2 Runners, Wrist Pulse** Kendall/Hunt Publishing by Ron Franklin
2 Cyclers From Jeff Stine/National Sports Center for the Disabled. Printed with permission.

Chapter 6 | **Sit and Reach Test, Quadriceps Stretch, Partner Assisted Stretch, Upper Body and Torso Stretch, Neck Stretch, Triceps Stretch, Chest and Biceps Stretch, Shoulder Stretch, Lower Back Stretch, Three-prong Support Side Stretch, Hamstring Stretch, Groin Stretch, Shin Stretch** Kendall/Hunt Pubishing by Ron Franklin

Chapter 8 | **Hamstring Curl, Silhouette, Front Curl, Grip Strength, Isometric Exercises, Adding Weight, Variable Weight Machine, Tighten Barbell Collars, Standing Lateral Raise, Shoulder Shrug, Upright Rowing, Push-up, Knee Push-ups, Pull-up, Negative Pull-ups, Reverse Curl, Two Arm Press, Triceps Press, Wrist Curls, Reverse Wrist Curl, Bench Press, Flies, One-arm Raise, Upper Back Lift, Kneeling Knee Tuck, Bent Knee Sit-up, Incline Board Sit-up, Side Leg Lifts, Half-Knee Bends, Leg Extension, Heel Raiser** Kendall/Hunt Pubishing by Ron Franklin
Blind Rockclimber From Melanie Stephens/National Sport Center for the Disabled. Printed with permission.

Chapter 9 | **Family Meal, Drug Store, Cooking Vegetables, Diet Diary** Kendall/Hunt Pubishing by Ron Franklin

Chapter 10 | **Screened Photo, Triceps Skinfold, Weight Scale, Biceps Circumference, Eating Habits** Kendall/Hunt Pubishing by Ron Franklin
Wheelchair Tennis Player Doug Gifford

Chapter 12 | **Drug Store, Writing a Letter** Kendall/Hunt Pubishing by Ron Franklin

Chapter 13 | **Screened Photo, Jogger, Rope Jumping, Basketball** Kendall/Hunt Pubishing by Ron Franklin
Handcrank Bicycle From John Weiland/National Sports Center for the Disabled. Printed with permission.

Chapter 14 | **Sit and Reach Test** Kendall/Hunt Pubishing by Ron Franklin